BUGGED
Writings from overhearings

'Inspired and inspiring'
Maggie Doyle

'Inside, outside, this project had me doing it everywhere....
Bugged has to be the best fun I've ever had in a public place –
with my clothes on.'
Sarah James

'Eavesdropping can lead to wonderful, quirky work. Bugged
is one of the most fun projects I've ever done.'
Cathy Bryant

'It's got me listening and looking again.'
Andrew Philip

'So many different types of writers have taken part.'
Janet Jenkins

'I thought this was a great idea, it gave me permission to
snoop about and listen to other people's secrets.'
Anon

To eavesdroppers, writers –
and to all who submitted work for Bugged

First published 2010 by Bell Jar
in association with CompletelyNovel.com

Bell Jar
Unit G7a, Venture House
Cross Street, Macclesfield
Cheshire SK11 7PG
www.jobell.org.uk

Designed by FOX - www.foxcreate.com

A CIP catalogue record for this book is available
from the British Library

ISBN 978-1-84914-053-9

10 9 8 7 6 5 4 3 2 1

Writings from overhearings

Edited by Jo Bell and David Calcutt

Finding poetry in the landscape

Bell Jar

Contents

Names in bold were specially commissioned by Bugged.

Foreword

On July 1st 2010, writers all over the UK went out on a mission. They looked as if they were going about their normal business. They caught buses, they went to the gym, they sat in offices or waiting rooms, they met people in the pub. But on this day, they were listening intently: *Bugged* was a national experiment in creative eavesdropping.

It was all our fault. 'Go forth,' we said to the creative community, 'and listen to people talking. No, really, you're allowed. Write something based on what you hear. Send it to us. The best incoming work will be shared immediately on our blog, and the very best pieces will go into a book.' We commissioned ten professional writers including Stuart Maconie, Jenn Ashworth and Mil Millington. Then we simply spread the word amongst the best story-writers, dramatists and poets we know, and released them into the community.

They didn't need telling twice. Writers are by definition inquisitive and indiscreet. Their key skill is to notice things and on July 1st, they went out and noticed like mad. Overheard fragments came in thick and fast to our Facebook page – some mundane, some heart wrenching:

'No Nathan, he's dead.'

'Have you received a bear in the post this morning?'

'I've put three pork chops on top of the fridge.'

'And as soon as I heard Michael Jackson was dead, I thought, "like f**k am I keeping that suitcase."'

Reading the resultant poems and stories, it is sometimes very clear what the writer overheard. On other occasions, a perfectly ordinary turn of phrase became a spark for something fantastical or sinister – no wonder the richness of material that was submitted, given the odd things that people say in the street.

Some of their overheard snippets appear in these pages to amuse you, but the finished pieces are published without the quotes which sparked them off. These strong, elegant and idiosyncratic pieces of work need no derivations to explain them. Trust us, every one of them began with a furtive writer making notes in a coffee shop or on a train.

Bugged reminded us that the streets are heaving with raw material for writers. It gave contributors a starting point that was not of their own making. The resultant mix is a breathtaking, exuberant selection of voices. Established writers appear alongside new poets and story writers whose names you will soon know better. Some pieces are funny, some wicked, some touching. All have an equal claim on your attention, and we are grateful to them all for joining our experiment. We also thank those many capable writers whose work didn't make it into this final cut: nosy Buggers of the UK, we salute you. Finally, we must thank Cathy Bolton of Manchester Literature Festival and Sara Beadle of Birmingham Book Festival, both of whom gave us prompt and unquestioning support when we needed it most; and Anna Lewis of CompletelyNovel.com, who so expertly and painlessly eased us into print.

Perhaps this organised eavesdropping leaves you feeling squeamish. Are you unnerved by our small invasions of privacy, by this twisting of innocent words into new meanings? If so, there is good news and bad news. The good news is that we have changed names and other details to protect the not-so-innocent. The bad news, dear reader, is that authors do this all the time. Pay close attention to the words of the writers in these pages. After all – they may have been listening to you.

Jo Bell and David Calcutt
www.bugged.org.uk

Tiny poet on bus
Helen Addy

Mother,
Big sister,
Little sister;
shoulders lulled together by hills.

'Moon, moon!' cries Little Sister.
Mother leans but cannot find.
Big sister follows dimpled finger to nothing;
her voice sweet and clear.
'Maybe the circles of rain on the window
are tiny, tiny moons from far away.'

They quieten;
chewing sweets and pulling on coats.
We get off together;
the sickly sky emptied of rain.

Grief
Sara-Jane Arbury

It woke me up this morning.
Naughty.
It knows it's not allowed on the bed.

Watched me all through breakfast.
Those hang-dog eyes.
No tit-bits. It'll get fat.

It keeps nudging me. Bumping its
nose against my knee. Once
it licked my hand.

I throw a stick to get rid of it.
But it brings it back, wanting more.
It won't leave me alone.

It teases me. Rolls over and
plays dead. Then gets up again.
Whines for attention.

I can't help stroking it.
Making a pet of it.
It owns me.

Could you resist it? Could you?
With its offer of love?
Limitless love?

The wrong sort of shoes
Jenn Ashworth

The newspapers said she wasn't right in the head. Nonsense. There's nothing more normal than a woman feeling like life's passing her by unless she's had kiddies of her own.

And the security in here's a joke. Two doors, one camera and a buzzer you push to get in during visiting. Us midwives have swipe cards but in an emergency there's a spot you kick on the left side and it's usually enough to jiggle the mechanism. That's a secret we let the new ones in on after they've done their probation. A reward for getting through the first six weeks – the night shifts, the stillborns, other people's mothers-in-law.

We take turns, sitting on that desk by the front door and buzzing the visitors in. One woman came just as I was leaving my spot.

'You'll not get much of a visit now,' I say.

I knew the sister in charge – kicks everyone out the second the little hand touches the half hour. The rules is the rules.

'Are you sure?' she says to me. Posher than we usually get.

They got me to describe her, later on. A raincoat. A folded brolly dripping onto the laminate. The raincoat was a soft fawn colour, the same as her wet-blond hair and her puddly, empty eyes. Only special thing about her was her shoes. Six inch heels, shiny gold straps. If she had a car she certainly wasn't driving it herself. So she had a man. Nice for her.

It might have been the rain on her face that made me think she was crying, but I felt sorry for her. She didn't look the type to be breaking into cabinets and pocketing the diamorphine, so I thought it would be all right.

'Leave it an hour,' I said, 'till Sister's gone home. Give it until eight. There's a spot here and if you knock it with your foot,' I showed her, 'it pops open.'

She stared at my feet as I was doing it. They're very strict about the sort of shoes we wear. I go to Clarks myself. What you lose in fashionability you make up for in price, durability and comfort and you can quote me on that – but that's by-the-by.

'Get your lady to draw the curtain round. You'll be all right for half an hour,' I said.

The woman smiled at me and went on her way. I carried on with the discharges and felt pleased. I put myself in her shoes – glad she'd not come out in the rain for nothing. I went off shift myself, shortly afterwards. Home to a Marks and Sparks ready meal and a docu-drama about Susan Boyle. I went on the internet and ordered her CD. Bed before eleven because I was on an early the next day.

The sound was something to remember. One of them wakes up, takes a peep into the crib. It's empty. They'd sliced her open to get her baby out and we'd never heard a peep out of her but this morning you could hear the screaming as far as oncology – even some of the cardio nurses came running along the corridor to see what was up. And this is maternity, mind – they're used to the noise of screaming coming from down here.

It was a girl, if I remember right. The police were there within the hour but there was no trace. Unprecedented, the papers said. Got to be an inside job.

I never saw that woman again but they played the securi-cam footage of us in court during the inquiry. I wore my other shoes to court – a brown coloured court shoe, funnily enough, with a low chunky heel that's wide enough to be comfortable walking, but not so wide it looks matronly. I had a blue two-piece and my mother's pearls and while you can't say I looked like a movie star, everything was clean and paid for and I think I turned out all right.

The thing is, I'd have said, if they'd have given me chance, it's these women – desperate for kiddies of their own, who'd make the best mothers. Some of them have been collecting tiny clothes for years, decades even, by the time their chance comes along. And compare that to the sort we get – teenagers screaming for me to bring them a bottle of formula so they've got time to put their make-up on before their feller turns up. You know the sort.

The mother of the missing child had another one the year after – she was young enough. Security's tighter now. Visitors have to sign in, sign out, have their names and faces checked against a list.

They never found her but I like to think the woman in the gold shoes has a house somewhere in the countryside. Big old place, and it's not empty any more. So many kiddies she doesn't know what to do with herself. Her happiness overflowing. I get a bit of it, second hand. Warms me when I think of her.

I had to leave. My last day, I open the locker to change my shoes and what's in there but the most expensive, shiniest looking pair of heels I've seen in my life. I'm not the kind to wear things like this – they're dancing and dinner shoes. Dating shoes. Nights out on the town shoes. Impractical. Couldn't hoik a baby into this world or keep a woman out of the next, wearing shoes like this. They were siren red – we all know what that means.

I put them on, walked out of the ward and into the rainy car park for the last time, smiling.

To carry it now
Andrew Bailey

If, within your brown paper,
whatever it is wriggles,
it is alive, a moth in the cage
of your hands. That is
a heartbeat, a countdown,
the clasp of a birdcage
breaking. Time then,
whatever your levels
of preparation, to own
what it was you wanted.
How it wriggles. Let it go.

Brenda loves knives
Mollie Baxter

1968

Brenda sat by her bed and checked her knives. So far she had eight, like birthday candles. Through the folds of the curtain, if she leant just so, she could catch a glint of moon. One eye closed, nose to handle-tip, she turned the dinner knife, looked down its length, noting the serrated teeth and a few soap drops dried to cloudy circles. She gave it a buff and placed it on the carpet with the others.

From the opposite bed, she could hear shallow breathing and the tiniest shuffle of a foot. Her sister.

Brenda pushed beneath the mattress, drew out another knife. She smiled: a favourite. The cheese-knife.

Such a brazen shape, the dipped blade, the two sharp points for puncturing. She pressed her thumb to each, one, two.

'You should not have them.'

The voice was tremulous, trying to be authoritative. Brenda looked round. Meryl was a disembodied head above bed sheets, eyes wide moons, the tops of two hands clutching the duvet like mouse paws. Brenda turned slowly back and touched the knife points to her tongue.

1974

'Meryl, you look *lovely.*' Mum and Nana beamed. They were all in the kitchen. Meryl stood in home-sewn dress, frilly socks and an Italian scarf she'd saved up three whole months of pocket money for. 'Doesn't she, Brenda?' Mum prinked a sleeve.

Brenda grunted and kept sharpening her pencil.

'And to think they might take you on permanently.'

Meryl's cheeks flushed with pleasure.

'They said I was a very polite and well-presented young lady. With an eye for *couture*.'

'Fancy,' said Nana.

It was only a Saturday job. Brenda tested the point. There was an inch of pencil left. She recommended sharpening.

'Brenda, stop that!'

Mum yanked the sharpener from her, pulled a key from her pocket and went to the knife drawer. 'Must I lock *everything* away?'

1975

Dinner time. Pork chops were always a trial, because the plastic cutlery couldn't cut the fat. Mum tried to look unconcerned, Meryl, as usual, had the expression of a martyr, but Dad's face grew steadily red with rage. He sawed at his meat until it skidded across his plate and his knife snapped.

'That's it! Give us the key.'

Mum met his glare.

'Jim -'

' - Don't!' His slab of a hand shook. Mum handed it over. He unlocked the knife drawer. Excitement fizzed in Brenda's belly and she tried to crane her neck to see past him. They were all in there. He spun round, a knife jabbing in her direction.

'And *you*! Don't you *dare*!

The meal continued in silence. Brenda could barely swallow her food. The drawer was still open, crammed with blades: fruit, bread, butter, dinner – even the hand axe from the garden - all gleaming.

'We filled in our work experience forms today,' she said, patiently hewing her chop.

Meryl went pale.

'You've not... you're not coming to the boutique, are you? You know you'd hate it. They only invited you out of politeness, because of me.'

Brenda looked neutral. 'No. Not the boutique.'

Meryl sagged. Even Mum looked relieved.

'Where?' asked Dad, his cheek balled with chop.

'Gregory's.'

Mum looked perplexed, then stiffened, 'Not the *butchers*?'

'That's a *boy's* job,' said Dad, his eyes like marbles.

Brenda shrugged. 'No such thing. Mr Blake said so. Anthony Hampton's doing hairdressing.'

Dad sucked his tongue and dropped his cutlery. 'I'll be in the shed.'

He pushed out his chair and Mum jumped to scoop up his knife, take back the key and relock the drawer.

Brenda's eyes fell on the two snapped halves of plastic knife.

Such clean, new edges.

Her mouth watered.

'Mum!' Meryl's voice was urgent.

Mum looked round and lurched forward, whipping up the broken plastic and slipping it into her apron pocket.

Brenda's eyes flashed hatred and Meryl squirmed like a rabbit under a claw.

1996

The circus tent was full. Sawdust steamed. Libby, the journalist, sat ringside with her photographer. This story would make her career: Two orphan sisters taken in by the circus so many years ago, but under what circumstances?

The dwarf band - tuba, drum-kit and vibraphone - struck up a fanfare. The spotlight blazed down on Madame Blade, dressed in electric blue mask and black, sequinned leotard. Across the arena, her eyes locked with Libby's. The crowd roared. She gestured across the arena to a wooden backboard where, cowering in bodice and tights, her wrists and ankles strapped to the board, was Meryl. The crowd knew the stories, all eyes sought out her left hand. Where five fingers should be, there were only three.

The photographer smirked. 'Don't give up the day job.'

Libby quirked her mouth.

'From what I can gather, Meryl's the lucky one. No-one else left in that family.'

He leaned in. 'What do you know?'

Libby shrugged. 'This might be Madame Blade's last show.' She threw a glance his way. 'Get a good shot.'

He fumbled with his flash.

Madame Blade called for volunteers. Libby scanned the crowd. It took her too long to realise the helpers were making straight for her.

'No, thank you, I didn't ...' But they didn't understand, just escorted her to the board. She saw a second set of cuffs, felt hands fastening her wrists and ankles. She shook her hair from her face, looked at her companion.

'Your fingers. How did ...?'

Meryl whimpered a laugh. 'Same way as my ear.'

Libby strained. Meryl watched with glassy sympathy. 'Won't snap. Buffalo hide. She's getting ready to throw.' She huffed a breath like they were sharing a park bench. 'So... What did you do?'

Libby swung her head. 'What?'

'It's important. Who does she hate more right now - you or me?'

Libby's eyes bulged.

'I *demand* to be..!'

But the band drowned her out.

'This is *crazy*!'

The music peaked, the crowd sucked in its breath. Through the glare, Libby saw Madame Blade raise her arm and swing...

Write what you know
Jo Bell

It's a standing joke at the pub quiz; *Aye aye, Stationery Dave's in tonight. Keep an eye on that pen mate, or we'll have nothing to write with before the picture round comes up.*

GOT A PEN, BOB? someone asks me too loudly, when David shuffles into the bar straightening his tie, as if it were a court appearance. Most people look around them as they enter a pub. David doesn't even look at the barman as he orders his tonic water.

Someone answers for me. NO, IT'S GONE MISSING. FUNNY, THAT.

Oh, give over, I say as they start up. *So he's got a thing for pens. Could be worse: could be crack cocaine or Dale Winton. Leave him be, the poor sod. He's doing no harm.* The picture round comes up. I don't have one on me anyway. Never ask a writer for a pen.

David sits upright in his tweed jacket at the corner table, sipping his tonic water, turning a pen over and over in his hands, frowning. There is always a pen: a cheap tube of plastic, or an elegant cylinder of brushed steel. Always a little notebook too; a thick oblong pad with perforated pages. He lays them out on the round brown table and steels himself with a swig of tonic water. I know the small rituals of the writer: and David is no writer. He looks as if he's sitting the most important exam of his life, in a subject he hates. He slowly scribes a word or two in the book – strikes through it, flushing and rubbing his face – tears the page out carefully, tucks it into his inside pocket. Takes out a different pen. Starts again. His jacket gets bulkier; the pad diminishes to a spiral-bound table mat; the pens build into a little bundle. Occasionally he looks up. It's the look of a rabbit in the middle of the road.

Why come on quiz night, if he's so antisocial? I ask the landlord. The place is bound to be heaving.

But of course the people are all in teams, heads down,

absorbed.

Besides, says the landlord, *it's the only night when there are pens lying around.* It's true – pens do go missing if you leave them on the table. It's a small town, so we know that he does it everywhere. The girl from WH Smith caught him at the door once. His pockets were bulging with gel pens – Uniballs in pink, yellow, lime green, like a bunch of headless flowers. She gave him a ticking off and let him go.

There's something about him, she said. *It's not his fault. You know.*

But I don't know: until I leave after a lock-up one night, and start the walk back along the canal. He's on a bench, staring towards the bridge. It's late. Even the ducks around his feet are sleeping. David doesn't look like he gets much sleep. We've never spoken, but I take a breath and say *Where do you live, mate? I'll walk you home.* He follows like a lamb. I wonder if he was waiting for me.

At his bungalow, I accept the mumbled invitation out of curiosity. It's an occupational hazard. You collect material. I'm collecting material as soon as I'm inside, like a burglar: clocking the photos on the wall, the shrine-like display of a teenage son in a home-made tank top with a Millennium Falcon under one arm – and then we step into the living room.

Bloody hell, David.

Every surface is covered with them; the corner shelves, the crazy-paving hearth, the mantelpiece over the gas fire. The bookshelves are packed with raggedy shoe boxes: the drawer handles are spotted with ink and I can guess what's in every one, because I can see them everywhere else. Great bundles of clear plastic Bics, clotted with blue ink. The ubiquitous Parker 25 that you got when you started work in the 1990s; dozens of them stacked in their boxes like little coffins in a vault. There are heavy-barrelled heirlooms, Montblanc or Cross fountain pens with deep blue lacquer and textured gold. The fruit bowl is heaped with bullet-slender ballpoints in 1950s turquoise or maroon. A vase is crammed with chunky 1980s pop-art biros.

In the pick-up-sticks scatter on the table, I register my own contribution; a translucent RAC freebie that went missing in the pub last month. It all brings to mind the Leeds Armoury Museum: the ranks of gleaming blades arranged by size or date, all different but all made for the same purpose. You could weep, really. You could weep.

David – What happened? Look at me for a moment. What's the story?

He does not look at me.

It's not a story, he says. *It's not a story.* And he takes me back to the little triptych of photos in the hallway, and he tells me his story. His voice is quiet, as if reading to a child. His tale is quick, unsparing and told with a kind of wonder – how odd that it should all still be true. How odd that the details should be so sharp, when the years might have had the grace to blunt them. The forest green jumper his son was wearing: the CND badge they showed him at the station. The motorway junction number. The height of the bridge. The make of the truck.

He focuses on a piece of air two feet from his nose: leans forward into the dado rail with splayed fingertips, as if testing its strength. His voice is shaking: the tendons in his hands are taut like guy ropes as he mutters his question. When I ask him to repeat it, he says it too loudly.

Can you write this? A pause, then quietly; *I've been trying myself. I have been trying. I have been trying. But I can't.*

And I say *David....*

He looks right at me. *Can you write this?* he asks.

I can try, I say. *I can certainly try.*

Rondeau redoublé
(Words in italics were found on a London train)
Julie Boden

Travelling to London and home again
city commuters are on the attack
packed into carriages, feeling the strain,
stuck in the groove of a regular track.

Leamington Spa-Marylebone and then back
through Banbury, Bicester. Each stop has a name,
but faces are nameless who make up the pack
travelling to London and home again.

Framed in the windows, eyes flicker back pain,
they chew on regret and lament at the lack
in marriage, of children, the house built in Spain.
City commuters are on the attack.

He feels for his brolly, she fingers her mac.
Squeezing on tubes and then smudging through rain
their lives are locked cases crammed onto the rack,
packed into carriages, feeling the strain.

Good girls go to Heaven, bad girls take the train
to gold dig the streets and spend nights on the craic.
Bold words on their tee-shirts repeat their refrain,
stuck in the groove of a regular track.

Bad girls go to London, they're singing *Love Shack*,
spreading their legs – *Mind the Gap*– to complain
of *tosser* and *losers*, the ones you can't jack
in *cos men aren't that bad when you've pickled your brain.*
Travelling to L.

It's all up in the air
Ruskin Brown

Alright Mush, how's it going? Said how's it going? Yeah not bad mate not bad. Just off to me sister's, nowt special. Yeah. What you up to? Good idea. Don't blame ya don't blame ya. Ha ha ha ha. And the rest. Sally? She's a dark horse in't she? She's always real quiet but Christ almighty. Dan bought me a triple whisky and she just like reggae danced over and picked it out of his hands and downed it in one, unbelievable. I said oi that was a triple whisky that and she went oh sorry and went and got me a single, real innocent like. Yeah weed in the car park! And oh yeah I'm just remembering these little miniature absinthe bottles in her bag these little green bottles Jesus Christ. Oh my head's like a vice man, fucked. Hopefully get some fresh air, clear it up. Yeah. I know, I know. About Rufus. Well I'm worried about it but he just won't listen anyway so what's the point? I told him straight he should knock it on the head completely, just stop now and come home. Ten days! Mate, he met her ten days ago, no I swear on your life mate, ten days he's known her. Student. One of his classes. English yeah. And now he's like all this we're in total love and I'm meant to be with her and all this and I'm like oh for fuck's sake, get a grip of yourself man, she's married! Yeah married Mush married. No proper married, she's like from this strict Muslim background. Don't know, don't know but like, he's saying oh it could be so dangerous for her if her family find out and all that, you know. Yeah! No, it's serious man, serious. I said I don't want to make assumptions about her culture and all that but I don't think they do amicable divorce in Turkey. What like come and find him and cut his head off or something? Ha ha ha. No but you can't mess about though can ya? Jesus. Ten days. To her, yeah, definitely. He's like I don't know what to do I don't know what to do I said just stop being such a fucking prick, that's what. He rings me from a phone box in Istanbul at one in the morning going now she can't get a passport without her husband finding out and we're gonna have to do this and we're gonna have to do that and I'm thinking this is just off the script. Joe's telling him follow your heart and everything will work out blah blah blah. Yeah. All that. Peace and... I know it's true, in a way, follow your heart but Joe just...yeah. He doesn't know what's really going on. You can't just follow your heart follow your heart. Just cos you want something....yeah that's what I mean, forbidden fruit. I bet she's gorgeous and it's like when something's in front of you and you want it but you can't, and it all goes mental. Anyhow I've had enough of it now to be honest, I'm just like, I can't be doing with it, someone else sort it. I think either Holland or Germany to be honest. No not Argentina. I wish I'd put a tenner on Germany when I thought of it back in the groups, six to one it was. Ha ha. Yes ve are so vell organised our defence is impenetrable. Ve are a force to be reckoned vith. Ha ha. Ok bud see you at Joe's later then, sort me bike out? Yeah nice one. Cheers mate. See ya. Later. Ok. Bye.

The biggest problem
Cathy Bryant

Crowded carriage,
the usual uncomfortable swaying.
Clutching each other amid strangers.
She turns to him:
'Do you realise what the biggest problem in our relationship is?'
Oh darling, so not the time nor the place,
say so many faces, wary, worldly,
but also wondering what his answer is
and whether it's what she thought;
and we wait, while he squirms and shifts
and the train goes thunketa-*thun*keta
and the people sniff and cough
and pass the time of day.

'Well', he replies, 'Given that everyone here can hear us –
I'm going to say my inadequate penis size.'

– and a great laugh breaks from her,
and the whole carriage smiles
as if it had filled with balloons and cake
and friends.
'Actually', she says lovingly, confidingly,
'It's your cat allergy.
 But I think we'll find a way to cope.'
And you can see the pink hearts floating around them,
and the train goes thunketa-*thun*keta,
rolling cheerfully on.

Let go
Dorothy Burgess

I hear a voice saying, *She could pass,*
the weighing-up practised and precise,
That one could pass for forty, when she tries.

Escape, for now, the ghetto of old age.
Evade time's cruel three line whips.
Time makes collaborators of us all.
Live the lie.

Then I hear, *But she's let herself go.*
And immediately I like the sound of this. Oh, let go.
Begin the long slide, take your pleasure on the way.
The joy of pushing off and speeding up, applying no brakes.
Go.

I am legion
A dramatic monologue for one or many voices
David Calcutt

Listen –
Wait –
The first thing I remember is –
The first thing –
No – Wait –
Just a minute –
The first –
I'm lost.

There's a lot of roads round here. They've all got different names. I live in one of them. One of these roads. It's got a name. One of these names. But I can't remember what it is. That's the thing. I can't remember. What the name of it is. The road. I'm trying to find it. I think it's round the corner. At the top of the hill. I think you turn right there and it's that road. Or left. You turn left. Or you carry straight on. I can't remember. I went to the supermarket. I had to get something, and I went to the supermarket to get it. And I got it, it's here in this bag. I remembered that, I remembered what I went to get from the supermarket, but I don't remember the name of the road where I live. I don't remember where it is, how to get there, there's so many of them and they've all got these different names –

Wait –
What – ?
No, wait –
The first thing I remember is –

– it's quiet isn't it what are you up to this week you owe me fortyfive pounds don't make me laugh all that money on a wedding you buy it then you just throw it away life of riley that's what you've got mate come here I said come here now can you hear me I can hear you I should think everybody can hear you I can hear everybody –

What – ?
Listen –
I remember –
The first thing -
Wait – wait – just –
I remember –

The first thing I remember is waking up in the road. I was lying in the road. A road like this. But it wasn't this road. It was another road. Early in the morning. Six or something. Earlier. Five. The sun was just rising. There was nobody around. Except me. And a woman. There was a woman. I heard her first. She said something, she asked me what I was doing, and I lifted my head and then I saw her. She said to me, What are you doing lying in the road? I told her I didn't know. I must have passed out. Because that's what happens sometimes. I pass out, and then I wake up. You pass out? she said. Yes, I said, I pass out. How often? she said. How often do you pass out? Is it a regular thing? Does it happen a lot? More than you'd think, I said. More than you'd believe. She asked me where I lived and I told her I didn't know. I couldn't remember. I couldn't even remember who I was. Well, what do you remember? she said to me, and I told her, the first thing I remember is waking up in the road –

Wait –
What's that – ?
Listen –
What – ?

– what's that you're saying what's wrong with you why are you talking to me like that have you heard yourself you're shouting why are you shouting at me well you never told me before it's irrelevant you're just trying to take control of my life that's it that's the end that's the end of our conversation I'm not talking anymore I'll speak to you later goodbye –

Wait –
Stop –
Where am I? –
Where was I? –
Listen –

I was in the road, on my feet now, not lying down anymore, and this woman was talking to me, she was saying, Don't you remember anything else? I don't remember anything, I said. I wanted to go because it was starting again, I could hear it starting, but she looked at me a bit puzzled and then she said, I know you. I know who you are, she said. No, you don't, I said, and she said, Yes, I do, I've seen you before. I know you. You're that alky, she said. You're the one who's drunk all the time. It was starting and I was trying to get away but she kept on. I saw you in the supermarket, she said. You were singing. You were drunk and singing in the supermarket. That wasn't me, I said to her. I've never been drunk. I've never sung in the supermarket. Look, I went to the supermarket just now, to get something, and I wasn't drunk, I wasn't singing. I just went to get something and I got it and now I'm on my way back, but I can't find my way back because I can't remember the street, the name of the street, there's so many and I'm lost –

Listen –
Listen –

She was just going on. And it had started and it was just going on. And it wouldn't stop. And she wouldn't stop. And I said to her I said to her I said –

Stop –

– sometimes there's one and sometimes there are many I hear them it starts quiet then it gets louder too loud all of them going on going on at the same time and that's when I pass out because it's too loud and too many and then I wake up and I can't remember who I am who I was before it's always somebody different first one then another everybody nobody and then it starts again quiet then getting louder too loud all of them going on –

Stop –

Wait – just –
listen –
The first thing –
It's quiet –
Listen – listen –
I remember –
I'm lost –
All these roads -

Listen –

We are many.

Black widow
Helen Calcutt

Imagine her
A sack of night in her skins
Trembling her scent

Her drop. The little gem cap
Dangled from a crack
In limbo, turned
Lopsided

Little demon
The size of a nail quick

Rubs her sticky legs
In the sticky light
Spicing her pincer lick

For heart-stiffened lump of sweet
Solarized
To suck at –

Eye-sack fists
Wet berried, gnat-souled

Gather in suspense
Here, sideways

The silks-in-water shadow; sails
Beautifully

Turning
Like a bent clock
And kissing
Mid-air dance before collision.

I grow old, I grow old
Mary Cutler

I was sitting on the top deck of a bus – always a good place for eavesdropping – when two Birmingham school girls got on. I can't say listening to the conversation of Brummie school girls counts as eavesdropping. You wouldn't have to drop very far from any eaves to hear them. Birmingham girls, from state or private schools, whether modestly attired in head scarves and trousers, or with school skirts hoisted so high you can read the label in the back of their knickers when they walk up the bus stairs, have one thing in common – loud and carrying voices which they are not afraid to use. I once overheard – I use the term loosely – one complaining she had fallen out with someone because 'She was always chatting my business', despite the fact she herself was chatting her own business at a decibel level that could be picked up by incoming aircraft to Birmingham International.

So these two girls got on, and, as is their custom, made quite sure we'd all be in on the act by sitting at opposite ends of the bus to conduct their private and intimate conversation. My own ears pricked up. I had this piece to write. My luck was in. Well, said – shrieked – one – that's it. I've dumped him. Just couldn't take any more. Not after what he did. (Great.) Why, what did he do, asked – bellowed – her friend. (This was the stuff.) Oh, you can read all about it on my Facebook page. I can't be bothered going into it all again. Do you want to get some chips? I'd certainly had mine. I couldn't read about it on her Facebook Page. I'm not on Facebook.

It's sad to be a social outcast. I don't want to sound immodest, but I never thought it would happen to me. I'm from a large family, I'm still in contact with twelve of my school friends – if the Net's down we just shout to each other across England – and, in one case, Wales. Apart from university, I've always lived in Birmingham, and the Midland writing community is close and friendly. Or it was.

Until I started falling out of the loop. I missed publications
– readings, performances, workshops. My friends would say,
'But it was on my web site – all in my blog – written up in
Facebook'. And it wasn't just people's work I was missing out
on, either.

*Scene; Boxing Day party given by hospitable and generous
friends X and Y. I am talking to another friend, the multi
talented J.*

J	Are you coming to X and Y's New Year's Eve party?
M	They haven't asked me. I wasn't sure they were having one.
J	Oh. (EMBARRASSED) I think they are.
M	Are you going?
J	Er – yes. They must have meant you to come.
M	But they usually mention on their Christmas card. Or email.
J	I can't think now how I heard about it. But I'm sure –
M	Maybe they want to keep it small this year –
X	Oh, J, while I think about it – can you give me a hand with the food for the New Year's Eve party?
J	STILL EMBARRASSED) Of course. Mary was just wondering –
X	(TO ME) Oh, you are coming, aren't you?
M	Yes. If you ask me.
X	(CONFUSED) Sorry. I just assumed.... Of course we want you to come.

Generous hospitable X, of course she did. But I'm old, I can't
just lurk outside houses I usually go to parties at with my
nose pressed against the window, like Cathy in Wuthering
Heights, to see if they'll let me in. I need – what's that
old fashioned thing called? – an invitation. And I'm sure

generous and hospitable X issued one. On Facebook.

The modern world is leaving me behind. I heard some Uni students on the train – see, I haven't forgotten this is supposed to be about eavesdropping. They were musing on the Distant Past.

Student 1	How did people manage before mobile phones?
Student 2	I don't know. You couldn't do Uni without them, could you?
Student 1	No! I mean, how would you meet people? You'd have to, like, say you were going to be at a certain place at a certain time!
Student 2	Yeah, and then be there! Unbelievable!
Student 1	I know. How would that work? (They laugh)

Mobile phone? My family didn't even have a land line. The hours I've spent in draughty phone boxes. Or writing letters – remember letters? Much though I love it, no-one writes page after page of emails, do they? Or treasures them for ever. Oh, you can save the ones that mean a lot to you. Until your computer crashes. It's not that I don't understand the appeal of these new technologies – I totally do. If I was a teenager, I would be poking my friends every half an hour, and texting them every ten minutes, though to my anxieties about not having a boyfriend, and not going to the right parties – bit of a theme here – would have been added worries that I didn't have enough Facebook friends, or people didn't text me back fast enough. But I'd have loved a blog. I wouldn't have had to write three unpublishable autobiographical novels if I could have had a blog!

This is great project, such an imaginative and inclusive use of all this new stuff, and I was very flattered to be asked to contribute. I'm happy to offer my thoughts and my words. But as anyone who has looked at the web site will see, I don't have many links – not virtual ones, anyway. Time's winged chariot is breathing down my neck – I haven't got enough real time left to make them. If my friends are going to break up with someone, I'd still rather they told me Face to Face, than read about it on Facebook. Because, as I found out on that bus, you can't eavesdrop virtually.

'I got brain freeze.'
Steph Dale

SCENE. A MAN is sitting scrunched up, leaning against the wall of a lift. A young GIRL is looking at the buttons; she runs her finger around the outside of one of them.

GIRL   You're sure none of them work?
MAN   This ain't going nowhere.

            The GIRL presses all the buttons.

GIRL   Used to have nightmares about being
            stuck in a lift. Nightmares about
            being trapped like this.

            The GIRL stops and listens.

GIRL   Someone's coming.

            They listen.

MAN   Nah.

            The GIRL presses another button.

MAN   Will you sit down!
GIRL   Sorry.
MAN   Get some sleep! Morning will come
            quicker.
GIRL   I can't sleep.
MAN   Used to better?
GIRL   At least a pillow.
MAN   'At least a pillow'.

            SHE settles then sits back up again.

MAN	Stop thinking about it!
GIRL	Can't. It was horrific.

The MAN stands.

GIRL	What you doing?!
MAN	Need to ...

MAN	*undoes his fly*

GIRL	Not in here! Go outside!
MAN	We'll lose the heat. It's friggin freezing out there. Besides, this is my house, my rules.

The MAN urinates in the corner.

GIRL	Jesus.
MAN	Told you, I force the doors once to get in and once to get out. Don't want anybody else spotting this gaff.

He completes his task and does his fly back up.

The GIRL picks at her fingernails. Pause.

GIRL	My fingers are going blue, look. (Beat). What time is it?
MAN	Late o'clock. Go to sleep.

Pause.

GIRL	Why do the suits have such a problem with us?
MAN	Papers tell them we're scum.
GIRL	I'm not scum. Got grade eight piano by the

	time I was eleven.
MAN	(Beat). How long you been out and about?
GIRL	Two years. You?
MAN	Nearly twenty.

Pause.

GIRL	Ta for getting me away from the fighting.
	Ta for letting me share your lift. It's nice.
MAN	Apart from the piss.
GIRL	But, really, what time is it?
MAN	I dunno. I don't have a watch.
GIRL	It must be six?
MAN	Nah.
GIRL	There'll be a clock on the ticket machine.
MAN	It got bust when the kid in the suit was beatin' up on old Tom.
GIRL	(Beat). You OK?
MAN	I got brain freeze.

The GIRL takes a packet of half eaten Rolos out of her jacket.

GIRL	Want a Rolo? I robbed the suit's Rolos. Dropped on the floor when he was smashin' up your mate.
MAN	Ta.

They share the chocolate.

GIRL	The suit will be in a nice, warm bed now. Sleeping and farting off the Christmas spirit.
MAN	Yeah.

Pause.

GIRL	What's your name?
MAN	You choose.
GIRL	.....Robert... Nah...St Nic. You look like a Nick.
MAN	Whatever.

They huddle.

Archimboldo's son
Marilyn Donovan

Hi, Dad, I forgot to say the code
for picking Sigmund up is... Parsnip.

Parsnip! I hiccup disbelief
skim the eye of the twin-set opposite.
We both snigger. It would have stopped there
except...

Parsnip! his wife shrieks as if to make sure
we all have heard. *You've chosen that!*
She wobbles, titters, blurs into a giggle
and soon the whole carriage rollocks
with laughter, wave after wave raking
its length as fields, hop-bines, a boy
safe in his absurdity unravel behind us.

I can't resist, twist to catch a glimpse
of this couple so slap-dash in their naming
and, having seen, imagine...

 an etiolated shoot
: elbows and knees knobbed as his father's
: hair finely-rooted as his Mum's

growing, good-as-gold, back in Dover
believing he is loved.

Bug in a pub
Lucy Douglas

Woman 1	Shall we or shan't we?
Woman 2	We ought to be good.
Woman 1	Bottle or glass?
Woman 2	Oh, go on then.
Woman 1	Bottle of house white, please, and two glasses.
Woman 2	But only one.
Woman 1	Yeah, yeah. So have you looked at it?
Woman 2	Yeah. Could be difficult.
Woman 1	Well, it's the men, isn't it? Pratt, Bunting, Air-Hair-Lair, Frog.
Woman 2	Straight PC.
Woman 1	Oh yeah.
Woman 2	Well, Boyd's away, Colin won't, Ian can't, Mick's on holiday on the night.
Woman 1	David?
Woman 2	Unreliable.
Woman 2	But good. Top up?
Woman 1	Uh huh. Thanks. Gregor?
Woman 2	Very straight. But getting better. Oh look, there's Morgan.
Woman 1	Morgan! Here, come over here a minute?
Woman 2	Morgan, can you do accents?
Morgan	What sort of accents?
Woman 1	Posh? Frog? Cockney?
Morgan	Yeah.
Woman 2	Well, go on then.
Morgan	What, now? What shall I say?
Woman 1	Anything.
Morgan	What ho, old chap, pass the port. Zees is ver' ver' nahce port, eet weel mak ma moustache curl ver' beautifully. Gor blimey, what a shirt lifter 'e is, innee?

Woman 1	Brilliant. You'll be fine. What do you want to be?
Morgan	In what?
Woman 2	This play? Posh old buffer, frog art dealer or Cockney scam merchant?
Morgan	Oh … well, I don't mind.
Woman 1	Great, we'll tell you when we've decided.
Woman 2	Good stuff. 'Nother bottle?
Woman 1	'Spose. What about the women?
Woman 2	Elizabeth Thing's the main one. Fiona?
Woman 1	Not Ascot enough. Sara?
Woman 2	Not flamboyant enough. Gael?
Woman 1	Too good. Jacqui?
Woman 2	Too short. Sandie?
Both	Nah.
Woman 1	I'll do it.
Woman 2	You'll show off. I'll do it.
Woman 1	Pot. Kettle … top up?
Woman 2	Thanks. We can do them. You 'n me.
Woman 1	What, all of them?
Woman 2	Well, how many are there?
Woman 1	Four. No, five.
Woman 2	Any dead ones?
Woman 1	Yeah, one quite early. Only one big part, Elizabeth posh and Cockney thing.
Woman 2	Well, I can do that. And dead. What does that leave?
Woman 1	That's nice wine. Pass the bottle. Knitting woman, boring wife and stuffy niece.
Woman 2	Well, you do them. OK? Sorted?
Woman 1	Yep. Sorted.
Woman 2	Apart from Bunting and Pratt.
Woman 1	Well, yeah. Apart from them. And the other two men.
Woman 2	Yeah. But fine otherwise. Great. Shall we have some crisps?

Cage on the Armley gaol bus
Ian Duhig

"...ee,
ahm not
SAYIN owt,
ah said,
ahm just
sayin..."

And that,
said this
composer,
is poetry.

Been a lot of ferret theft
Jo Field

They slink like a sleekness of water
silver and sable past the mind's eye,
hob and jill and kit flowing easy
under lintel, across sill.

They're picking over the family plate,
scraping its polish with spiky claws,
passing it back along a chuckling queue
with practised paws and wicked grins.
They're stuffing sacks, making good
their masked escape.

A dark-eyed white is in the driving seat,
scouring the tarmac, scorching the night
with the hot spoor of rubber, trailing
a disorderly flounce and hitch of tails
from flapping doors.

They crack their sharp triumphant smiles.
No more tinned food, no litter tray, no trousers
to be thrust into and thrashed around in
like a bag of snakes. No more manhandling
through rabbit holes, or miles of plastic pipe
or cardboard rolls.

At Dover, an albino waits with passports.
The loot is portioned: to each as much
as he can carry. In the musky mist of dawn
they're doing the weasel war dance,
bopping and barging and bumping
on the Dunkirk ferry.

Overheard on Gyllingvase beach
Marilyn Francis

You said it never snows in Cornwall.
Just like that. No argument. Never snows.
Along Gyllingvase beach the sky turned black.
I heard a swimmer say, 'the water's andsome in December,
it's only when your teeth get cold it's too late.'

At night we huddled in your sister's single bed as ice spread
over the inside of the windows and our breath froze over the
counterpane
and only the sea stirred in the polar bear darkness.

The last I heard
A story in three parts: I
David Gaffney

My prawns texted me to say that they would be out of date in 12 hours, so I rang Alfie, but he was grumpy and didn't seem to care. If your shellfish sent you a message, he said, it means they are still thinking about you, so you shouldn't worry.

But I do. Now I will have to rush home and stuff down a warm mound of degenerating seafood – alone, because Alfie prefers Morecambe bay shrimps or scampi. And freezing them is out of the question because stocking up on supplies makes me feel like I'm preparing for a post-apocalyptic dystopian future.

The prawns talk to me, everything talks to me. Each one of my household objects is in constant communication all day long and for some reason Alfie, who works at home since the cafe concession failed, finds this annoying. It's not that I'm all that desperate to know everything he is doing all the time; the information the objects send me is useful in other ways. For example if Alfie eats a tin of tuna I get a text saying we're down to one can, or if he flips on a light I get a notice that power usage is increasing, and if he lies down on the bed I get a message from the duvet about cleanliness. It helps my planning. But I must admit that I do also find it comforting to receive minute by minute accounts of his every move. It's a little like being God. And what weirdo doesn't want to be God?

As I got closer to home the urgent, red-coloured messages from the prawns dried up and my mind flooded with horrifying images; Alfie may have covered up the microchip with a tea-towel – he'd done that before – or worse, chucked the whole thing into the waste disposal where the communication chip would be minced up with fish flesh and nothing would be heard from it again.

When I got home Alfie was waiting in the hall, wearing his chef's hat and black and white check trousers. He kissed me on the lips.

'It's all ready for you,' he said, and took me into the kitchen.

Youth
Sarah Gallagher

(A young lad is chatting on his phone.)

Nah, nah, nah, it was insane man. We was completely f****d.
Yeah it was wicked, you 'ad to be der man. It was mental.
What?
Nah, nah, she loved it. She was s*** faced. She was like
'waaayyyyyy. I'm f***in' well f****d'. Fallin' all over da place 'n
I was like 'what you playin' at woman? Get off da floor.'
Dunno. Shoved her in a taxi innit. Stupid cow.
Huh? Yeh . . . Smithy, Bruiser, Big Dave, Switchblade. Yeh, da
whole crew was out innit.
Ha, ha. Yeah. Smithy was mental. He nutted some k**b 'n
chundered right outside da kebab shop. Nutter.
Yeh. Proper messy night innit. F***in' quality night man. You
'ad to be der.
Anyway mum was ringing to say I ain't about for dinner
yeah?
Cool. Safe. Laters.

A day out
Roz Goddard

So we're sitting there, in the park, on a tartan blanket, Suzie's bought a pork pie, a baguette, butter and a trifle, and she's laid it out, as if we're normal people. Her whole life she's had this thing about wanting to be normal, it's important to her. I keep telling her she is normal, she lives in a house, she's got a window cleaner, she buys trifle. Anyway, that day she was trying too hard. I've said to her, it's like she wants to trim the edges of life. She had a job on her hands that morning when she picked me up outside the prison. I'm basically hyper, hysterical when I get in the car, I start counting trees, then I'm going on about how loud everything is and I can't get over the number of good looking men walking about.

'I'm changing the radio station Andrea,' she says,' let's see if Radio 3 can calm you down.' I'm still gawping at how fast the women with the shopping trolleys are walking and I'm not coping well with the breeze on my skin. And the birds, don't mention the birds, since when did they have so much to say? I sometimes think Suzie is the only person in the world who isn't afraid of me. I know she isn't because I can read expressions. I'll say something outrageous to get a reaction and she'll just look at me as if I'm a silly kid looking for attention. 'What you need to remember, Andrea, is I have seen you sharing bath water with a dog and your weekly wash. I cannot be shocked by anything you do.'

Fair enough. So we're sitting on the grass eating pork pie, which is disgusting. 'Suz, this pastry tastes like it's been left out in the rain.' I was grateful that she'd gone to the trouble, but as she would admit herself, going to the park was not her best ever decision. For one thing there was too much sky and for another it wasn't the most sensitive thing in the world to take me to a place where courting couples were snaking over each other in the sunshine, as if all that mattered in life was love and kissing. Frankly, she shouldn't have come to pick me up in a car that colour, she shouldn't have taken that left turn through the estate, it might have been better all round if an organisation had stepped in. Someone from an organisation would have taken me to an office up a few flights of stairs and given me a cup of tea, it would have smelt of paper and photocopying, there would have been phones going off every two minutes, it wouldn't have been so emotional. But Suzie's the saving type and she thinks everyone deserves a second chance.

There's music from the tiny radio and I'm picking daisies and arranging them in a square on the picnic blanket. I'm afraid to look up in case anyone recognises me, or more likely recognises Suzie, who is, I'm imagining, 'well known' in the area. She gives her runner beans away in the summer. Always grows too many, for that purpose, to give them away. If, heaven forbid, she died and a reporter camped outside her place, the description of her house with its shining windows and riot of geraniums in the front garden would conjure up the warmth and self-respect of the woman. I don't deserve her. Would anyone recognise me? The only way might be the way I walk, you can't alter that can you? The jizz of a person.

I shall get over this, this not wanting people to recognise me because I will tell anyone who asks that I stabbed my boyfriend to death, in his Ford Capri, on a country road where there were no street lights and tried to blame it on a road rage incident. Just not today, with the pork pie and trifle sweating in the heat, it's not right. And the dogs and the sun and Suzie flicking her hair back and wearing her sun hat on a choker round her neck. I've come to terms with it. His face is quiet now, there's no movement in his eyes and his lips are closed, he has nothing to say to me. When he appears in my head, it's like he's in a photograph having a pleasant day out, not a fabulous day, but a pleasant one.

Coming out of prison, being picked up on the cobbles in front of the place and being driven to the park with the flowers and dogs and footballs made me feel ill. 'It's the sun,' says Suzie, 'let's move into the shade.' I'm looking at her with a kind of awe, as if she's an angel. I'm starting to laugh and the grass is a crazy green, like it's been laid out for a film, and there are arms in the air waving and catching balls and there's a girl doing a handstand and her red skirt is turned inside out like a tulip and you can see her dark knickers. I am suddenly a dog myself, sniffing the ground, Suzie's pet on a leash, a dog she can't let off in case it savages a kid. I'm drinking juice from a carton and looking at the pork pie and I'm seeing pearls in the meat. 'That's the tasty bit, the fat, eat it, it's lovely,' and that's Suzie sounding so tender, like my mother. I am a kid again, at the fairground on the spinning tea cups and my insides are in a mixer travelling up to make their way into the air. A dog comes over and starts licking my toes and he has some pastry off Suzie who is laughing with the owner and I'm in sawdust somewhere or straw, an animal lying down in the heat, squirming and suddenly I'm howling and no-one knows what to do.

This is the time
Susannah Hart

This is the time and the place
Of the small pleasures, of the weak coffee and the iced bun.
Well, you've got to treat yourself a little
When you're my age, haven't you?

This is the time of the special offers at Sainsbury's
And the deal at the Morrisons fish counter.
I must admit I do like their goujons,
But they're a bit expensive for what they are.

This is the time of the grumble, the mumble,
The lapsed season ticket and the highlights on the telly.
Poor Derek! Hasn't made a game since April.
Course everything changed when they moved to West Ham.

This is the time of the arthritis, the flat shoes,
The bus passes and the help with the central heating.
Lots of 'em could do a day's work but they don't;
I told Eileen, you take what's yours.

This is the time of potatoes in allotments,
Of thinning out and failed sweet peas.
My children all went to school here
*But there's too many of **them** about now.*

This is the time of closing inwards, of folding up,
Of staying put and shutting down.
I saw one once, on the train to Wimbledon –
Black down to here, and then glasses, and black all the way
down.

This is the hour in the morning
When we've come to where we were going.
This is the time and the place.

How to develop new audiences
A story in three parts: II
David Gaffney

Alfie and I met one year five months and two weeks ago. At that time he was the chef at Ballet Rambert's café concession and I was head ballerina in a production of Swan Lake with tractors. Before Swan Lake with tractors Alfie used to complain about the cafe concession all the time.

'These fuckers in tights eat nothing all day,' he would moan. 'A Mars bar, a diet coke and three fags is their entire daily diet.'

'But I'm a fucker in tights,' I told him.

'I thought you were with the tractors,' he said.

The addition of tractors to the production was a massive boon for Alfie's café concession because the tractor drivers, six heavy-set men with faces like boulders, rocked up every day and ate like rats. They started on full English breakfast with black pudding and fried bread, then at lunchtime they had liver in gravy with chips, or steak and kidney pudding the colour of a dirty vest with mashed potato and a viscous green sauce. Now and again they even had an evening meal as well, sometimes Lancashire hot pot followed by baked Alaska, once three bean chilli with half-and-half rice and chips and a chunk of Arctic Roll. Alfie really had a chance to shine. The other ballet dancers and I would watch the six tractor drivers ladling down gristle, fat, sugar and pastry while our tongues lapped in and out of unfeasibly tiny portions of yogurt. It was like watching a dirty film.

But Swan Lake with tractors was only a moderate success and although Alfie tried to persuade the artistic director to employ heavy machinery in other productions, it turned out to be a blip.

Alfie, however, stayed on, and every day he fed me oat and cranberry slices, chocolate coated flapjacks, Fentiman's ginger beer and French pink cloudy lemonade. One day I bought him a tatty old Ladybird book about tractors from Save the Children and he laughed. 'We both need big strong men in our lives,' he said, and placed the book on the counter for everyone to see.

Vulnerable
Angi Holden

'The problem with Margaret is that she's too open,' says Janet, firing a St Luke's Hospice price tag into the designer label of a neatly folded cotton blouse. £3.99. 'It makes her vulnerable.'

Susan takes the blouse and slips it onto a hanger. It's her size. She considers the colour, a pale shade of blue. She hasn't worn blue since her ex told her it didn't suit her. Maybe it's time for a change.

'I'm not sure...' she says.

'Really?' Janet looks up from the next item, a pair of cream linen trousers. 'I'm certain of it. Did you hear her talk about that man the other day? Whatever his name is.'

'Robert,' Susan supplies.

'That's the one. She doesn't know him from Adam.'

Susan folds the trousers in half, and slips them onto a suit hanger. She is certain she saw a matching jacket in the same donation bag. She wonders absently who Adam is. She hasn't heard Margaret talk about him, but she certainly seems to attract the gentlemen.

'And she invited him home last week to help with some paperwork.' Janet shakes her head in disbelief. 'Financial stuff, she said it was. Well, I told her, you have to be careful these days. Not trust every Tom, Dick and Harry who turns up on your doorstep.'

Susan looks at the embroidered lace basque, which has come from the same bag of clothes. That would bring the Tom, Dick and Harrys to the doorstep, she thinks. It is midnight blue with pale pink top-stitching and it seems at odds with the floral blouses and linen suits. It's not the sort of thing she'd ever wear of course, and she dithers, uncertain whether to put it with the underwear or the evening clothes.

'She shouldn't be discussing financial matters with just anyone,' Janet continues. 'You hear such dreadful stories about people taking advantage of elderly widows. There was an article in the paper the other day....'

Susan's attention wanders. She is used to working with Janet and has heard her opinions on the subject before. Many times before. It's easy for Janet to say, of course. She has a husband in robust health, and a couple of married sons who both live locally. For widows like Margaret or divorcees like herself, both childless, both new to the area, life is different. A bill drops through the letterbox and you have to deal with it. And if you don't understand something, you look for someone who might be able to help. A friendly face, like Margaret's Robert.

'.... And the police don't hold out much hope of catching the man, so he'll just go off and prey on some other poor, unsuspecting old lady.'

'I don't think Robert's like that,' says Susan, emerging from her reverie and suddenly aware that some response is required. 'He seems so nice.'

'Huh!' grunts Janet. 'I'm sure that's what they all say.' She passes across the soft pleated skirt she has just priced up - navy blue, Principles, a snip at £5.99 – and presses her hands into the small of her back. 'Time for a brew. Tea or coffee?'

'Coffee please,' replies Susan. She has worked alongside Janet every Friday for the last six months, and occasionally alongside Margaret over the past five weeks. Strange that Janet never remembers that she doesn't drink tea, whereas Margaret asked once and never forgets. 'White, no sugar,' she calls after the retreating back.

She looks at the clock. There is a light drizzle in the air, and there haven't been many customers today. It's not her usual day in the shop – she prefers the busier Friday duty - but she likes Margaret and is happy to fill in for her. A pity about the seafood salad, she thinks, checking the time again on her watch. If she hurries after the shop closes, she'll be able to get some flowers from the Co-op on the corner and call in on her way home. See if Margaret needs anything.

'I expect Robert will be there,' she says, as Janet returns

carrying a small tray.

'Be where?' asks Janet, putting a mug in front of Susan. 'You expect Robert will be where?'

'At Margaret's.' The steam spirals from the hot liquid. She can smell it is tea and she moves it carefully to one side, making room for the last few garments. She tips the bag onto the table, and passes a charcoal cardigan to Janet for pricing. The style is comfortable, familiar. There must be dozens of them about, she thinks.

'Probably,' says Janet. 'He's the type to take advantage when she's unwell.'

As they sort through the remaining clothes – nice things, barely worn – Susan thinks about her new friend. She wonders if she's as defenceless as Janet seems to think, wonders whether Robert could indeed pose a danger. He seems so polite and reassuring.

As if conjured by her thoughts, Robert pulls up opposite the small parade of shops and climbs out of his shiny blue Vectra. He looks weary as he walks across the car park.

'Talk of the Devil,' Janet mutters under her breath.

The bell on the door chimes as Robert comes into the shop.

'Margaret's not in today,' says Janet, pre-empting the question. 'She rang in sick.'

Robert crumples into a chair by the bric-a-brac and books. He leans forward and rubs the heels of his hands against his eye sockets.

'She's gone,' he says.

Susan slides the cardigan onto a hanger, remembering Margaret wearing it the previous week.

'She's gone,' Robert repeats, his voice flat and matter of fact. 'And so has all my money.'

Chinese whispers
Andy Jackson

Course, he never did treat her as well as his first wife.
Course, I heard that he beat her, as well as his first wife.
Course, he was dead meat according to his first wife.
On the court he was deadly, according to his first wife.
In court he was deadly, according to that midwife.
They thought he was dead, according to that midwife.
They thought he was dead in the hour before midnight.
They found him there dead some time after midnight.
They found him there, dead, there in broad daylight.
They found him on deck, there in broad daylight.
They found out his debts were only a fleabite.
They found in his desk a note by the breadknife.
They found the old fool cut his throat with a breadknife.
The old fool. The note said he'd lived such a sad life.
The old fool is dead, but think of his sad wife.
I heard the old fool liked a drink. Like his first wife.
I heard that he beat her, as well as his first wife.
Course, he never did treat her as well as his first wife.

7am rising
Sarah James

Silence: only the air conditioning, talking
in whispers, the shower's exotic pelting
after the pool's icy plunge
and a hairdryer's sudden sirocco –
minus the sting of sand.

'Sorry!' Someone bumps into the air.
Ghosts do not say 'Good morning!' –
they've been up all night already,
shy away from the glare
of artificial light; small talk.

'You off to work?'
Splash! The question bombs the changing room.
Water jumps. But there's no reply:
the ghosts have just finished their shift
and the lockers still aren't awake yet.

Cool box
Lucy Jeynes

I have a cool box
That used to belong
To the Bay City Rollers.
It is not tartan
Nor even check
It's very plain.

In those days
Owning a cool box
Was cool.

I bet they drank
Double Diamond
For its wonders.
Or Irn Bru
For its gliders.
Icy cold.

They left it behind
After the gig
And I took it home.

At first I showed it off
Everyone wanted to see
But now it's ordinary.
It lives under the stairs
With a broken record player
And the Betamax.

I am a seagull
Charlie Jordan

Skateboarding the sky,
I glide over
a ghost pier
submerged in the past.

Below me,
masts clatter their applause
from weekend boats
rusting through winter.

Seeking tourists
to terrorise,
I hurl mussels onto tarmac
and swoop to snack.

'This is my beach,'
I remind the sea.
'Your tide owes me rent.'

Domestic science for boys
A story in three parts: III
David Gaffney

The head chef at the café concession in Ballet Rambert was never rushed off his feet, so Alfie used to sit in his floppy hat and black and white checked trousers reading superhero comics. One day between rehearsals I lied that I was attending a science fiction ephemera fair in Croydon which featured a guest appearance by someone out of Blake's Seven and asked him if he would come with me, and he agreed right away. I took Margaret from hats and over the next few months we attended dozens of these affairs up and down the country, and after every one, me and Alfie and Margaret from hats would go for a curry.

One day Margaret from hats never came and we never looked back.

The café concession was replaced by a Costa Coffee and Alfie decided to become a consultant advising other chefs on their business plans. He developed a website which featured an animated dancing baker and a clickable interface of kitchen utensils and he came to live with me, the idea being he would run his business from my front room.

I began to install the technology a few weeks after he arrived because I was puzzled about what he did all day in the house on his own. No one ever seemed to use the clickable interface of kitchen utensils. I keep a scrupulously tidy house and when I come home from the ballet I notice every minuscule alteration. One time the coffee table was at a slight diagonal to the sofa, and when challenged he just said he forgot to move it back. But why would you need the coffee table at a slight diagonal? Surely you could move it closer to the sofa while maintaining its parallel position? My mirror, the one and only reflecting surface in the house because of my adolescent weight problems, was on the floor by the wrong side of the bed. And under the wardrobe I keep winter woollies in a set of cardboard boxes and for some reason the lid from one of these containers turned up in the bin, torn into bits and smeared with jam.

I had to take action and short of hidden cameras I came up with installing the fully intelligent and interactive household management system which would hopefully tell me everything about what was going on.

Once I was home it was clear that Alfie knew the prawns had sent me a message. A delicious smell was coming from the kitchen. He had flash fried them in President butter, garlic and black pepper and had dressed the table with a white cloth and glinting cutlery and set out crusty French bread and chilli jam for dipping.

We sat down and he poured a glass of white wine into my favourite handmade goblet and a tumbler of water for himself and we clinked and said cheers.

'Aren't you joining me?' I said.

'No, thanks. I've had cheese on toast.'

I pulled a face.

'I used the dustpan and brush.'

'Thank you,' I said, wondering at the same time why the brush had not sent me its usual update about bristle clogging.

'That message by the way. It wasn't from the prawns.' he said.

'Oh,' I said

'It was from me. I wanted you to come home early because I think it's time.'

I de-shelled a prawn and smeared it with chilli jam. 'Do you think so?' I was trembling inside.

'Yes. It's time you learned to chop. And I have set everything out over there, ready for your first lesson.'

I looked across to the work surface. Onions, carrots, celery, peppers, cucumber, tomatoes and oranges were lined up next to a chopping board and his precious five hundred pound Global knife which I wasn't usually allowed near.

'Are you going to show me how to form my fingers into a claw?' I said.

'Yes,' he said.

'And how to cut without the knife leaving contact with the chopping board?

'Yes'

'How to do leeks?'

'Leeks as well.'

I ate the prawn and looked at him. I knew that when we began the lesson he would stand behind me and I would feel his breath on my neck and he would kiss my throat between chopping, and I would learn quickly how to cut up vegetables like a professional. This was the first thing. After this he would explain to me about science fiction. Maybe then I would be able to switch off the monitoring system, because once I understood his special chef skills and his expert knowledge of comic book heroes there would be no reason to mistrust him anymore.

The Four
Calum Kerr

It's like tig, only not. Tig was harmless and fun. Okay, sometimes it would get a little rough if you tigged someone and they claimed that you'd missed and carried on running. The argument could turn into a fight. But, hey, that was all part of it. We were, what, nine, ten? Something like that, so the fight was never anything more than rolling around getting some grass stains on our trousers that would make our mums shout. And afterwards it was back in for the next lesson, no grudges, no worries.

This is a grown up version of that, after all we're seventeen now, but it seems to be all grudge and worry and no fun.

It started when Andy started seeing Clare. Before that, we were solid, we were a group. We were The Four. When we said it, you could hear the capital letters. Brothers were never so close.

But then Clare came and did her Yoko routine and suddenly Andy was all, 'Can't make it, fellas, gotta date,' and 'Sorry I didn't make it. I got held up,' and 'I'm not sure Clare would want to.' So we had to get rid of her.

It wasn't about anything nasty. Just persuading her that someone else might be better. So we did our best to convince her. When Andy brought her along we would tease her. We'd arrange to split them up and then we'd tell her stories about the other girls he'd supposedly seen. All the conquests he'd supposedly made. We invented a whole harem of girls that he'd led on and then spurned. Eventually we made her so worried about him that she broke it off before he could hurt her too badly.

The Four was back.

But it only lasted a few weeks. Then Kyle started seeing Beth.

It was the same drill with her. This time Andy was in

the fold. Kyle knew what we were doing, but he couldn't stop us. I don't know if it was just that she was made of sterner stuff than Clare, or maybe Kyle had warned her what we were up to. Maybe Andy was just looking for some payback. Whatever it was, we tried talking him down, and when that did not work, Andy killed her dog. That did it. She didn't even split up with him. No properly. She just started to act as though he was evil. If he even tried to talk to her she screamed for help.

It all seemed quiet for a while after that, but that was only because Chris was keeping Emily from us. He knew what would happen if we found out, so he saw her in secret. It would never have come out if it hadn't been for the fire alarm being set off in the cinema. The lights came up automatically and as Andy left, he saw them getting up from the back seats, hand in hand, and pause to share a quick kiss before heading for the exit.

Andy and Kyle locked her in the basement of Andy's house for four days before they let her out. None of us saw her again. She was taken out of school and her family have put their house on the market. Word is they're moving to the U.S.

Once again we were The Four, but I don't think it can last. I'll hate to be the one to break it up, but I think I might need to move away too.

You see, Kristen keeps smiling at me, and it makes me feel good. I don't smile back when any of the others are around, but I know they've seen the attention she's paying to me. I want to pay her some attention back, but she'll have to be willing to come with me.

Chris told me last night that he's bought a knife.

Scar
Emma Lannie

The girl is moving to Filey, which is the end of the world. It is both The end of the world, and it is At the end of the world. She usually lets him hold her hand, but every time he tries, she slaps it away. They walk side by side. He watches her face. She doesn't have a smile. He feels trapped in a body that has to stay where it is, a body that cannot just up and move to Filey, no matter how much he wants it. She won't look at him, and when he tries to talk to her, she shakes her head and starts humming loudly. It is breaking his heart.

He stares down at his shoes. He thinks about how this will be the last time his feet are next to hers on a pavement anywhere. He thinks how they used to sit on her bed, their feet stretched out across the covers. It was only that one time, but it felt like the real beginning of something, and whenever he thinks of it, he feels the pop in his heart of something forever. He can't think of it as being only what it was. He knows she felt the things he did. The way she whispered into his chest and pulled him closer. The way she let his mouth devour her.

He remembers every inch of her skin. Every sigh. Every slow movement she made across the hours of that night. His body remembers, too, and he has to fight his muscles to keep them from reaching out and touching where they once were able to. Sometimes he is not quick enough, and his arm swings out to catch hers, his fingers intertwine with hers, and between them there is a bridge that lasts as long as she will let it. And she never lets it last long, but he is surprised by the length of time she does allow. Today it is getting less and less.

The girl breathes quickly. He wishes she would slow down, wishes they could stop, and talk, and maybe do more. Kissing her was always the best pastime. She never let it be mediocre. But now she won't look at him. He understands from the sharpness of her body language that she doesn't want him there. But the street is a free country, and he will walk wherever he wants. And if that means right next to where she is walking, then so be it.

She has a scar above her knee that she hides with skirts. It is a perfect slice across her skin, a faint, indelible line. He has one just like it forming in his chest, feels the blade of indifference cut into atria. It will be visible only on X-rays, he thinks. It will start off as a searing pain, and when he is admitted to hospital, doctors will stand round his bed talking in hushed tones, holding the X-ray up to the light, pointing along the scar with pens until he sees how lucky he is to still be alive. He won't feel lucky. He knows this.

She turns a corner and he stops. She continues walking. She is an arm's length away. Now it is a whole body's length. He watches the shape of her moving away from him, from the Us that he wanted to believe in. He shouts her name, but she doesn't look back. Without the weight of him beside her, she is fast. He won't catch her up now unless she stops, and lets him. He cups his hands around his mouth, tries to use himself as a megaphone, shouts, 'I won't see you after next weekend, ever again. Why are you being so horrible to me?'

In the distance he watches her feet falter, slow, but then she picks up the pace again. She doesn't turn back. He stands there, stuck, in his body. He once thought that he would follow her to the end of the world. But she won't even let him get to the end of the street. And inside him the new scar is forming, and all he can do is stay as still as possible, hope that the tear is clean.

'...he was dead long before the boy knew him...'
Pippa Little

Two women, words whipped over a shoulder
in a windy car park, don't see me listening
and vanish, leaving behind them
(stationary cloud of smoke
after a train's departure)
this man, this boy –

I can't ask either
to make any sense, have no right,
except in my mind, where
the dead man hangs around a little ill-at-ease
by the boy's elbow, near the breakfast table,
hoping he'll hear his name:
how it solidifies like clots and curls of grey
the white sky will eventually rub away.

Lacuna
Liz Loxley

Such lives do not echo down through the years
like those that were left: vibrato tamped down
by War. Blank certificates with a space
for the name: husband; father of the child.
No wife to relate how this unshaved cheek
pillowed hers in sleep, or how his first-born
filled in the gap between shoulder and jaw.
No child/grandchild to inherit his joy
of the jig and the fiddle, or to tell
how the swell of a violin rested
beneath his chin, or how, with the harvest
brought in under the ache of a blue sky,
he played his fiddle as the sun went down,
his boots clapping time on a flagstone floor.

What friends are for
Rob A Mackenzie

The grey, the concrete and canal,
the skyscraper trowelling
among stray flakes of cloud

so high residents laugh off
plans for neighbourhood watch
and instead wreck the lift.

The stairs are concrete,
the top sixteen flights
abstractions from street level,

who would climb so high?
Unopened envelopes litter
the lobby, mushrooms flourish

on every balcony – here,
lives become so self-contained
even we feel the urge

to knock for admittance,
but why bother when under
the guise of friendship

your ground floor flat can be
trashed and television ditched –
a demonstration of lightweight

humour, nothing serious,
just laughter in twilight
among friends. Take

the extra points and scuttle
up the housing ladder. Never
forget what we do for you.

Not a girl
Stuart Maconie

This train stops, not at Adlestrop,
but Meols Cop and Burscough Bridge and Tyldesley,
all the scattered halts and one horse towns
strung between the shy sea and the deckchairs at Southport
and the Sea Breezes and Decaffs of Manchester.

You could grow rubber in this carriage
and in the tropics of the rattling stock
of the hastily franchised train, tempers are fraying
like trackie bottoms off Oldham Market.

An Asian schoolgirl, books on lap, rests her head on the window,
and Bolton's embankments drift though her reflection
whilst all around her the madness of little men reigns.

Schoolboys, the kind of which
not more than three are allowed into newsagents
at any one time
playfight and roughhouse, hair jagged with gel,
green gold-crested ties slack and askew
swinging their Nike holdalls like sandbags

Hoodies trade blithe obscenities, their skins the colour
of cigarette paper and dappled with acne like cheap Anaglypta.
They lie lubriciously about what they have done to and with and
on girls with names like old lags fag coughs; Jax, Kaz, Raych,

A Golem of a toddler, his popped tube of salty snacks
snatched from his puffy hand by Mum
begins a slow, ominous crescendo, like an air-raid warning.
His lower lip pulses like a fish, he stalls his lungs
And the siren blossoms in the chip fat air.
Mum is nonchalance in budget bling. Dad thumbs glumly

in an earphone hiss. No-one comes and no-one goes.
The birds of Lancashire do not sing.

Suddenly Mum's had enough and hisses too,
into the ear of son and heir..

'You're not a girl.'

A bandsaw rasp as curt as a smack,
then back to 'We Love Telly', job done.
Son subdued and pink with surly shame.

The Asian girl barely stirs, hardly aware of those
who one day she will tap with stethoscopes and bring
the worst of news. Me, I am thinking of

a swan of a cellist playing Elgar's Concerto.
or East End Matchgirls caught in a flash of sodium
arm in arm, laughing at the sweatshop gates.
Or an ebony girl, as tall and slender as a bulrush
walking back to her village with a jug on her head,
as a 50s debutante learning deportment might balance
a book,
but nobler and lovelier, coming through the shimmering
heat of the Veldt, a mirage written in ripples.

And we pull into Piccadilly and spill like quicksilver
into a city of girls and the ghosts of girls,
suffragettes and Shelagh Delaney,
Mrs Gaskell and Elsie Tanner.

No, son, you're not a girl
worse luck for you and me.
And there's your birthright and your curse,
your lucky break, your epitaph
all there, overheard,
in your mother's offhand treachery.

Rumours
Ian Marchant

I live with my wife and stepdaughter in a flat above a hippy gift shop on a busy High Street in a small town on the border between England and Wales.

If I lean out of the window, I can see my local pub, all of two minutes' walk away. It's great if you want a quick drink, but it makes our bedroom catastrophically noisy at chucking out time; especially in the hot weather when we have to have all the windows open. It's a bit like living in a Soho loft apartment, though it's not a direct analogy, as our town has a population of just over 2000, and a high percentage of them are retirees from The Black Country. Still; this is the busiest part of our little town, and it can be noisy, in its own way. Overhearing chatty neighbours, local shoppers, and rowdy drinkers is our everyday and all night lot.

Last weekend, for example, a girl was standing in the street screaming at her boyfriend. Her screaming woke me up. I looked at my watch. It was 3am.

'Why did you fucking text her to say that we were splitting up?' I didn't hear her boyfriend's reply, as I rolled over and buried my one good ear in the pillow. But I expect that whatever his answer was, it contained a high degree of untruth.

We are in Wales, but only just. Opposite our flat is the Post Office, which declares itself the Last Post Office in Wales, though it could just as well be the First. Except to the west, where the Radnor Forest rises up from the valley of the River Lugg, we are surrounded on three sides by England. We get Channel 4, not S4C, our TV news comes from Birmingham, and our local newspaper is the Hereford Times. Hereford is our nearest city; it's where we go shopping, where we catch the train, and where we go for our hospital appointments. And our church is C of E, not Church in Wales, one of only four Welsh parishes which look to Canterbury rather than Llandaff for spiritual guidance. The border is a five minute walk away from us. But our neighbours feel themselves to be just as Welsh as someone from Merthyr Tydfil or Blaenau Ffestiniog. They support Wales at the rugby, they get misty-eyed when they hear a male voice choir, and they are huge enthusiasts for marital infidelity. As far as they are concerned, they are as Welsh as laverbread and Pot Noodles. I'm just not sure that people from other parts of Wales agree.

It's their voices which are the problem. They speak with a beautiful burr, much as you might imagine people on the Archers would speak if the actors really came from the countryside, rather than Solihull. Anyone round here who speaks with a Welsh accent is just as much an incomer as the retirees from Brum or the English arty farty hippies (of whom I am proud to count myself one). There is only one Welsh speaker, and that's Llynos, and she's from Cardigan. And she says she's forgotten most of it anyway.

The guy in the flat next to us is a proper Radnorshire lad, and he speaks with the local accent. His little place, not much more than a bedsit, is above a café, and is sandwiched between us and the flat above the local chip shop.

On nights when he staggers back pissed from The Farmers Arms, he likes to play his Fleetwood Mac Greatest Hits CD at industrial volume. I have to get out of bed and lean out of our kitchen window and bang on his kitchen window with a stick to get him to turn it down. Sometimes this works; and sometimes it doesn't, and then we lie awake while 'Rhiannon' or 'Tusk' throbs through our bedroom wall into the small hours.

'I used to like Fleetwood Mac', said my wife at half two-ish a few nights ago.

She's lucky. I never did.

Mr. Mac we call him. He came up to me in the street last week to apologise after the latest such incident.

'You know what it's like,' he said in his East Radnorshire burr, 'sometimes you've just got to crank it up and bang it out.'

I've tried to guess how old he is; I reckon 23. I don't think I'd mind so much if he played drum 'n' bass or dubstep like a proper 23 year old coming back pissed from the pub. At least it would seem appropriate. But Fleetwood Mac? Who ever cranked up and banged out Fleetwood Mac? And only ever Fleetwood Mac?

Pav, the chip shop owner. is going mental. His flat is on the other side of Mr Mac, and he and his wife have a new baby. I've heard Pav at two in the morning out in the alley screaming obscenities up at Mr. Mac's window; again, sometimes it works, and sometimes it doesn't. Pav and I were talking about it last week.

'Why fucking Fleetwood Mac?' said Pav. 'What's fucking wrong with him?'

'I dunno. Maybe his mum liked them, or something. Perhaps he heard it in the womb.'

'I tell you what.' said Pav to me this morning after another night listening to 'You Make Loving Fun' through the walls, 'I've got a really good mind to make him a Pink Floyd CD. At least I like Pink Floyd.'

It felt like my worst nightmares might be coming true. Not just lying awake all night, but lying awake all night listening to selections from 'Wish You Were Here'. I realised this afternoon that I needed to act, and quickly.

Tonight, at just after one, the music starts up.

BOM BOM BA BOMBOM, BOM BOM BA BOMBOM

I'M A MONSTER! GOT A REVVED UP TEENAGE HEAD...'

My wife sits up and clicks on the bedside lamp.

'What!' she says. 'What now! What's this? This isn't Fleetwood Mac!'

TEENAGE MONSTER! CALIFORNIA BORN AND BRED!'

I smile at her, only half awake.

'This, my love, is 'Teenage Head', by The Flaming Groovies.'

'I can't believe it! Are you going to bang on his window?'

'Perhaps in a bit....'

'What?! Why not now?'

'Well... this afternoon, I burnt a seventies compilation CD and stuck it through his letterbox. He seems to like seventies stuff. This is track one. I want to hear what the rest sounds like.'

'You did WHAT?'

'Well, if I didn't, Pav was going to do him a Floyd CD.'

'Go and knock on his window!'

'But... it's the Flaming Groovies.... It's a million times better than Fleetwood Mac... ten million better than Floyd.'

'Just go and make him stop...'

I get out of bed, pull on my dressing gown, and head towards the door.

'Stpd anka' says my wife.

'What did you say?' I ask.

'You heard.'

Soft music
James Mason

'I could wake you up with flowers and soft music;
it's much better than the sound of running water.'

No, think of the sass and sauce
in the sound of tides turning:
how shivers mark the sand
into bent staves, each one
loose as a snapped bowstring;

the crash of rain drops,
caught in slow-motion,
their sharp petals bloom
on impact then wilt in a
million small explosions.

Claudia, we are transformed
by water's soft music;
transfixed by colours it steals
from the sunlight and wears
as its own brindle tunic.

I would wake you now with
the sound of water to repay
the bright surge and chicane
I felt in my blood; the brine
rising in me yesterday:

my ears filled with the *toccata*
of taps in the house running
as every basin brimmed
with steam, and you dawned
from the bath, overflowing.

So, I guess you too are like water,
surging beyond the high seamark:
moon-pulled, wave-tossed,
how your kiss fizzed over me
and bobbed me along like a cork.

At a price
Lynsey May

Look at you with your complementary mixtures of auburns and browns, your practical haircut and your larger than necessary wedding band. I'm waiting for you to have the chance to judge me. I don't want to give that to you. But at the same time a small, and probably perverse, part of me wants to see the stutter on your tongue and a faint blush scudding across your cheeks.

I would have walked right past you if you hadn't had the presence of mind to step into my path. But, yes, isn't it funny that we've run into each other like this. One of those things I do agree. But if we were going to run into each other then this would surely be the street to do it on. And thank you ever so much for your compliments on my dress last night. Thank goodness you are the type that's far too polite to ask how I managed to get my hands on such an exclusive design. I know you know how exclusive, I could see that in the way your eyes skated from it to my face when I handed over my coat.

I should really decline your invite for coffee, but you're pressing me so warmly that you're doing a good job of hiding your loneliness. My hands are cold and I don't have another engagement until much later. I let you bustle me along, It feels as though your hand is affixed to my elbow, pushing me forward but when I look, it is casually pushing your shiny hair behind the ridge of your shoulder. I feel like giving you a nod of admiration but instead I answer your questions about the shops we are passing. Yes, I have been there, depressing selection I agree. Yes, terribly limited indeed. But aren't we lucky that there are all these shops to choose from in the first place and that we are the type of people able to afford the choice?

Of course I think Brian is handsome, in an unusual kind of way. You're right, I would hardly be seeing him if I didn't think so. You ask me question after question about him but you never wait for the answers, instead you flay me with information about your husband. I'm not sure what it is that you are looking for. I try to judge from what you say about

Brian, what he may have said about me. I have moved in and around lives like yours and I feel you should be easy to know inside and out, but I have to admit that there is something about your incessant chatter that intrigues me.

I'm sure I want my coffee black thank you, no it's not to lose weight, but thank you again for telling me that I don't need to. It's merely that I am not fond of milk. Of course I don't think any less of you because you've ordered a latte and asked them to only put half a shot of espresso in it – plenty of people have problems with caffeine.

I'd assumed I knew why we ended up in this sweet little café, I've had plenty of women looking out for their good, good friends in much the same way. Sometimes I avoid it, other times I let them talk – it makes them feel better about themselves. But as you fidget with the spoon, the sugar, the pale, beige foam of your coffee, I wonder if you have another reason. Maybe you are about to warn me, many men warrant a warning for one reason or another.

We exchange wry smiles as a baby begins to scream and I reassure you when you ask me not to judge you, but you just can't stand babies. I feel much the same way and I look at you anew, surprised that you have surprised me and you are sitting there rattling away, not really trying to find my secrets out but making me uncomfortable anyway.

You have something I don't have, and it's not the kind of thing that I covet but when I think of it I am uncomfortable. You smile at me and tell me I am beautiful and it is a strange thing to hear from a woman when there is no jealousy below it.

I'm not sure I need another coffee but it's too late, you are ordering more. I look at the flush at your collarbone and decide to go. Fuck Brian, he's a lousy tipper anyway.

I don't suppose Brian ever did tell you what I do for a living? I say sweetly, already gathering up my handbag and gloves. I guess not, it's hardly the kind of thing he'd want to admit to

You lean in towards me, still clutching your spoon and your voice is lower and slower than I've heard it.

I knew of course, you say, he didn't need to tell. What I need to know now though is, how much do you cost?

The Select
Mil Millington

Steve, Son of Tim: 'It is time! It is time! It is...'
Crowd of The Faithful: 'Time!'
Steve, Son of Tim: 'Signs and portents illuminate the hour. God's wrath...'
Crowd of The Faithful: 'long foretold, patiently awaited,'
Steve, Son of Tim: 'is come to sweep away the swarming evil of this sinful world. Only the Select shall enter the Ark. Only the Select shall see another sunrise. Only the Select shall return when the waters and the fires and the fiery waters have passed. Only the select shall build God's world anew.'
Crowd of The Faithful: [Cheers. Applause.]
Steve, Son of Tim: The Ark awaits!
Crowd of The Faithful: [Cheers. Applause. A single vuvuzela – mass 'Shhh's – vuvuzela stops. Cheers. Applause.]
Steve, Son of Tim: 'So, all the women, follow me!'
Crowd of The Faithful: [Cheers. Applause.]
Steve, Son of Tim: Goodbye!
[Cheers and applause gradually falter, fragment, and stop.]
Man #1 *(shouting from The Faithful)*: And when shall the men of the Select begin to board the Ark, Steve, Son of Tim?
Woman #1 *(shouting from elsewhere in The Faithful)*: And the two of each animal?
Man #2 *(shouting from the back of The Faithful)*: Two? Wasn't it seven? It says seven.
Woman #1: It says two as well. And... you know, two makes sense, doesn't it? I thought the 'seven' bit was a typo.
Crowd of The Faithful: [General murmuring of agreement.]
Man #2: A typo? It's inerrant. If it says seven in there, then it's *seven*. Or am I just being *too* Faithful? Because *I* followed the actual word of God, and I've been shovelling seven horses' worth of dung off my lawn for six months to prove it.
Man #3 *(shouting from elsewhere in The Faithful)*: You got horses? I got horses too. Wasn't somebody collating this?

Man #4 *(very distant)*: I got two horses, then another seven. I thought that's what it meant. Nine horses, in two stages.

Man #2: Oh, for... what did everyone else get?

[Voices from the Crowd, building up – 'Horses', 'Horses', 'Horses', 'Ants', 'Hamsters', 'Horses again – sorry', 'Geese', 'Badgers', 'Woodlice', etc. – until it's a roaring cacophony.]

Man #1: Excuse me...

[Crowd voices continue.]

Man #1 *(very loud)*: Excuse me!

[Crowd voices fall silent.]

Man #1: Excuse me. Sorry, but could we just return for a moment to when the *men* of the Select are to board the Ark? Steve, Son of Tim, when shall the men of the Select embark?

Steve, Son of Tim: Only women are in the Select, brother. Now, I think I can clear up this confusion about whether it's two horses or seven–

Man #1: Hold on: *just* the women?

Steve, Son of Tim: Yes.

Man #1: *Just* the women. And you.

Steve, Son of Tim: I was surprised too, when God told me.

Man #1: I understood men *and* women would be among the Select.

Steve, Son of Tim: It doesn't say that anywhere.

Man #4 *(testily)*: It does imply *nine* horses, though.

Crowd of The Faithful: Shhh.

Man #1: OK, no, it doesn't *say* it, explicitly...

Steve, Son of Tim: There you go, then.

Man #1: Well...

Steve, Son of Tim: But God's voice, in my head, *did* tell me it was, 'All the women, only!'

Man #1: Only.

Steve, Son of Tim: Only.

Man #1: In your head.

Steve, Son of Tim: In my head. That's right.

Man #1: When?

Steve, Son of Tim: Tuesday. No – wait. What's today?

Wednesday, it was Wednesday.

Woman #1: Shall we bring our two of each animal beside us, Steve, Son of Tim?

Man #1: Wait a minute, wait a minute. I still have a few questions about the Select being only the women and Steve, Son of Tim.

Steve, Son of Tim: It's not for us to question God, brother. But it might have simply been logistics. Imagine if I had to call out the names of each of the Select, one by one. It'd take *ages*, wouldn't it? And the clock is against us here, let's remember - what with it being Time, and God's wrath being come. God would have foreseen that issue, would he not? And his design would have included the solution. By all the Select happening to be women, it's a quick division and the whole process of boarding the Ark is simplified.

Man #1: Simplified down to you, Steve, Son of Tim, and all the women. God could have chosen some other distinction, surely? He could have said, um, 'All the white people.'

Woman #1: Nazi!

Man #1: Actually, I'm black.

Woman #1: Oh, I *see* – and that makes it all right to be a Nazi, then, does it?

Man #1: It's not about—Ugh. Look: I'm just saying that I find it really quite odd that Steve, Son of Tim, gets to go off alone with all of the, and only the, women.

Woman #1: It's not only the women. There's a lot of animals too.

Man #4 *(even more testily)*: Especially horses.

Man #1: If you bring up your nine bleeding horses *once* more I swear I'll come back there and–

Woman #1: Horses, women, white people – is there anything you *don't* hate? I think we know why *you* weren't among the Select.

Man #1: I do *not*—!

Steve, Son of Tim: Calm! Calm... calm. Can't you see what's happening here?

Man #1: What?

Steve, Son of Tim: It's obvious. Satan is testing you.

Man #1: Testing me?

Steve, Son of Tim: Yes. Listen, brother, you joined The Faithful because you read the Book and heard my words and knew that it was true, correct?

Man #1: Well... yes.

Steve, Son of Tim: And you've known that I have revealed the true will of God when I've talked to you about sin?

Man #1: Yes.

Steve, Son of Tim: And about the causes of all the problems in the world?

Man #1: Yes.

Steve, Son of Tim: And about what kind of shoes were pious and what kind God hates?

Man #1: Yes. That particularly.

Steve, Son of Tim: Then, brother, were not Satan sowing doubt in your heart, why would you question *this*? Let me ask you, what is more likely: that you're wrong to question this one thing, or that you were wrong about *everything* you've believed was true, for all these years?

Man #1: Hmmm...

Steve, Son of Tim: Everything you've believed, or this?

Man #1: Hmmm...

Steve, Son of Tim: It's *this*, isn't it?

Man #1: OK... I s'pose.

Steve, Son of Tim: Of course it is! Praise be to God, for re-opening our brother's eyes!

Crowd of The Faithful: [Cheers. Applause.]

Steve, Son of Tim: Now, as I said, all the women, follow me! The younger, prettier ones at the front and the older, uglier, richer ones towards the rear, please.

Honey
Emma Morgan

In the airport. Waiting for my mother. No book. No iPod. Purse in car. Mobile in car. Bored. So I eavesdrop. But nobody says anything because this is an airport and everybody is waiting for somebody and nobody knows anybody else and nobody does old fashioned things like talking to strangers anymore unless it's online. So I look at people instead. I think, for the manyeth time, why do really old people go in for those beige blousons? I am pleased with myself for remembering the word 'blouson.' And why is it that in an old woman you can see the pretty girl who still likes to do her hair nicely and wear things that involve flowers just like she did to tea dances in the forties, but in an old man all you can see is the BFG. I hope that the woman is called Vera though. I hope the man is called Ernest. Or Fred.

Then there is someone who I think is a gay man until I realise that it is a French woman with very short hair and that sort of androgynous thing about her which the French call 'gamine'. I am pleased with myself for remembering this word. I begin to hope that she is from Paris and that she is called Madeleine and that everyday she buys one perfect mille feuille in a pink box tied with a ribbon and feeds it to her shi-tzu whose name is La Petite Princesse.

Then there is a man with very large man boobs who is wearing a blue and brown striped polo shirt that is, and there is a sense of inevitability about this, too small. His name is Simon. For a living he... no, I cannot get to grips with him because I am too sorry for him. There is a pretty woman in a cotton shift dress that has no wrinkles who looks like she strokes her hair with silk of a morning and she is accompanied by a man who looks like he works in a tyre factory. Her name is Lisa, her partner is Rob, and actually they are brother and sister and not WAG and bodyguard.

There is a lady and her lovely blonde children who she bought from Boden along with a very nice jersey wrap dress. I am hoping she is called Constance but this is unlikely. She is probably called Penny and I bet she makes a lovely salad. Her husband is a banker or a lawyer called Mark. He is hardly ever home but when he is he is bullying Olly into the first eleven although Olly actually prefers Barbies. I am pleased with my new form of self entertainment, I believe it shows a certain inventive independence from the shackles of modern technology.

And then there is the middle aged man sitting in front of me. He is blind. I know this because he has a guide dog. He has a rucksack and a suitcase and a Labrador in a harness and I would like to say to him, 'Excuse me, does your dog really go on the plane with you? Where does it sit?' But then a woman comes up. A woman in her sixties in three quarter length trousers who I bet likes clematis and whose name is quite obviously Jane, and she starts manhandling the dog without even saying, 'Excuse me' or 'Can I stroke her?' I bet she wouldn't do that if it was a Rottweiler.

'What's her name?'
'She's called Honey.'
'How old is she?'
'Four years old.'
'How long have you had her?'
'About two years.'
'And is she your first dog?'
'No, she's my fourth.'

And Jane is doing that thing you do with Labradors where you rub the front of their throats and the rolls of their fur go forward and back and I hate Jane because I like doing that and because she is failing to ask that interesting question about where a guide dog goes on the plane.

'She's a lovely dog,' says Jane as she gets up to go.
'Yes, she is.'
'Bye.'
'Bye.'

And Jane exits as if this was a play and she was scripted. Stroke Dog. Ask boring questions. Leave.

The blind man talks to Honey.

'Good girl,' he says, 'you like a cuddle don't you?. Good girl.'

Now I am really stuck. I want to say 'Excuse me,' but I feel that I would be invading this man's privacy because I am a sensitive person unlike Jane who was just thick and rude. And now I want to ask all sorts of questions. Like 'Why are you blind, have you always been blind, what's it like, how do you train a dog like that, is it hard to get one, do you have to go on a dog waiting list? Where does Honey go on the plane?'

But now I can't ask anything, I have missed my moment and I am frustrated and I really hate Jane and now I also hate the blind man a bit, and I can't even think of a name for him or any kind of story, and then a lady comes, who is quite obviously his wife, and says 'Hello darling,' and takes the suitcase and the blind man picks up the rucksack and puts it on his back, which surprises me, though why I don't think blind people can carry bags I don't know, and he puts one hand on his wife's arm and another on Honey's stick harness thing and goes.

And then my mother comes through the arrival gate and starts talking to me about the luggage belt not working. But I am too pissed off to listen. And that is where eavesdropping and speculation and not having your mobile will get you. I go home and Google guide dogs.

Sonny
Ray Morgan

'I've started winking at dogs.
Sometimes, they wink back.'
The luggage tag that swings tantalisingly
under the Essex-to-London train seat tells me
his name is Sonny. Sonny, I imagine,
has dreadlocks. I cannot see any,
or smell any,
but I like to imagine.
Sonny's voice is light, playful,
he sounds the sort of man
who winks at dogs.
He says it to his friend with a
hint of 'I dare you' in his voice; urging,
'wink at one too, see what happens.'
The name from his tag, the
crusted heel of a sandalled foot
the dog chat;
it gives me a whole being.
This is a man who goes kite-surfing,
island-hopping,
does not own a TV.
He is fluent in Icelandic,
can breakdance,
knows a thing or two about real ale.
His home is all wooden floors,
spider plants,
dusty knick knacks from worldly travels;
a lingering smell of rollies.
He loves Bukowski,
his favourite book is Fear and Loathing
with Riddley Walker a close second.
He has long eyelashes,
arms full of golden sun-tinged hairs,

this man can juggle.
He can crouch, in board shorts,
salt-crusted cheeks from a day in the surf,
and wink into a dog's face.
He earns one in return.
He is a man of confidence,
a king among man and beast.

This is Sonny.
He winks at dogs.

Eavesdropping
Benjamin Morris

We should make popcorn, someone says,
and we all laugh, because we need
something other to do besides

stare. It's a rainy Sunday and in the flat
across the street our neighbours
are making love, him in his chair,

her on top, rocking gently back and forth
like a reed in the river wind,
still dressed but leaving no doubt

over what they're up to. We turn away,
turn back, and away again—and when
at last they finish, and see us there,

with our beers and our clumsy glances,
she starts to laugh, and shed the rest
of her clothes, him following suit,

and start right back up all over again—
this time harder, and faster, and louder,
so rending the air with their cries

that below them on the street
men and women quicken their pace,
lower their heads, shake their umbrellas dry.

It's always 11:15
Mil Millington

It's always quarter past eleven.

Always.

Quarter past eleven on a Thursday morning.

Time is as slippery as a polished enamel bath full of egg yolks. It has no objective speed, its necessary direction is questionable, and before the Big Bang it simply wasn't. The fundamental rules of is and must and could be are based on forces – nuclear, electromagnetic, gravitational – whose values are arbitrary. In your universe, a hatful of constants led to *your* universe; but yours is only one in an unbounded multiverse of variation. In infinite other universes, a minutely different value of the weak nuclear force means the stars can never ignite. In infinite other universes there's nothing, or not even nothing, or so much nothing that there's no room for everything. In an infinity of yet others the cosmos played out *exactly* as it did in yours, except Rome never fell; in another infinity the only difference is that ice cream tastes like gravy; in another Belgium is ruled by otters; in another pizza delivery flyers don't make up seventy-two per cent of the average person's mail; in another people can see only the colour blue so there are no wars because it's just too confusing with the uniforms and flags; in another there's a reason for opera; in another Piers Morgan was identified early and bricked up behind a wall.

But this isn't one of those universes, and it's not your universe either. In this universe something happened, and now it's always quarter past eleven on a Thursday morning.

Sophie's mug is white and has the name of a supplier of stackable chairs around its outside. As usual, the coffee in the mug is cold. Not stone cold - not so cold that you'd pour it away; it's exactly cold enough that you'll definitely drink it, but do so via a grimace and three, huge, medicine-brisk, 'Let's just get through this, OK?' gulps. Sophie isn't drinking it right now, however. The mug of coffee on her desk is less a beverage and more a statement, a symbol, a humanising magic charm. It gives a teacher multiple other levels; levels in which she's laid back – perhaps even a little counter-culture. 'If I were just some kind of robot with no life outside this school,' a mug on the desk announces, 'would I be *drinking coffee* in the classroom, eh?'

'Miss Rowlatt? Miss Rowlatt? I don't get this.'

'What don't you get, Ataxia?'

'This.' Ataxia power-slouches backwards as she pushes her exercise book away, like a resolute infant rejecting a plate of cruelly unprocessed food. 'All of it.'

Three rows behind, Taeniasis riffles a snort from his nose. 'It's a poem, stupid.'

Ataxia twists on him. 'I know it's a *poem*, you racist - I just don't get it. It's proper rank. Poems is supposed to be nice and that. This in't nice. There's snot everywhere.'

'It's not snot, stupid. It's slime and stuff. It's not snot, is it, Miss?'

'No, Taeniasis, it's largely frogspawn. But the poet chooses to—'

'Make it sound like snot.' Ataxia QEDs her arms across her chest in triumph.

Sophie is hungry. The emptiness in her stomach has started to bubble slightly. It's been ages since she last ate, but when she can eat next is still that little too far away. It's no help, gastrically, that she always feels like this.

'Do you not think the poem's funny, Ataxia?'

'Funny?'

'Yes. The poet is painting a comic picture.'

'Snot's not funny. It's gross.'

Taeniasis sighs loudly. 'It's not snot, stupid - it's *frogspawn.*'

'Your face is frogspawn.'

'The poet...' Sophie wonders if this is her sexual peak. One's sexual is going to *have* a peak, of course - that's a simple physiological reality – and, as a woman, it seems that's she's in roughly the right area for it. But there's no guarantee (in fact it's colossally unlikely, statistically) that one's sexual peak will fall at a moment when one is having sex. Or one is about to have sex. Or one can imagine a situation in which there's more than a sobbingly low prospect of any opportunity of meeting a man one would want to have sex with. Much more likely, it'll drift by at some indifferent moment; wasted, unnoticed and lost. Maybe this is it. Perhaps she is – right now - invisibly and to no use whatsoever, sexually peaking.

'The poet... the poet uses the word 'Naturalist' in the title, doesn't he?'

'What's naturalist?'

'It's like what David Attenborough is, stupid.'

Ague shoots his hand up. 'Miss!' Muscles strain against tendons in an effort to extend arm length. 'Miss!'

'A naturalist is someone who studies nature, scientifically – yes, Taeniasis, like David Attenborough.'

'Miss!'

'So the poet is giving us a grand title, but eventually reveals a little boy who's scared by some frogs and runs away. It's bathos.'

'What's bathos?'

'He was one of The Three Musketeers, stupid.'

'Your face is a musketeer.'

'Miss! Miss!'

'Bathos is when you deliberately go from something very imposing or serious to something small and trivial. It's funny. See? So, the poem *is* funny, isn't it?'

'Miss!' Ague's arm is whipping through the air. '*Miss!*'

'Yes, Ague?'

'My step-dad's name is David, Miss!'

'Well... there you go.'

'Can I use that in my answer, Miss?'

They should sell Sexual Peak Tests at the chemist's, Sophie concludes. Like Pregnancy Tests and Diabetes Tests and all the other Tests they have there. You should be able to pop into Boots and get a Sexual Peak Test – blue for 'Before', red for 'After' (perhaps a small display of flashing LEDs and a little music for 'Right Now'). Just so you'd *know*.

'Do you remember how we talked about exam technique and 'Always reading the question', Ague?'

'I've seen The Three Musketeers,' says Taeniasis. 'On DVD.'

'DVD? Man, that's so ghetto. We have Blu-ray.'

'Blu-ray's gay, stupid.'

'Your face is Blu-ray.'

'Right, that's enough you two. Let's all stay civilised for just a little bit longer, shall we?'

Dogs can smell medical conditions that people don't know they have. Can children – even when you can't feel it yourself – see that you're Peaking? God. Can they *see* it? Can they all *see* it? Will Ague put it in his answer?

Sophie glances up at the clock screwed high on the wall at the front of the classroom. It's quarter past eleven. She tries to control her breathing.

'Just a little bit longer, OK?'

High up
Lynda Nash

We're smoking weed on the old stone bridge at Ty Pant and Trev says, 'Remember Nibsey? He used t'walk on this wall single 'anded.' He strokes the side of the bridge like you'd smooth a dog.

'Yeah,' Milton says, 'single 'anded.'

'You can't walk single-handed,' I tell them. 'Unless he was walking upside down balancing on one arm.'

They look at me then at each other, eyebrows raised; Trev in his parka and bobble hat; Milton with his head shoved so far down in his denim jacket it seems as if he has no neck.

'Yeah,' says Trev, 'he'd jump up yer and he'd walk from there to there.' He stretches his arms out as if he's being crucified. 'Nibsey was like some fuckin' gymnastic. An' when he got the end he'd give a little jump and turn around and walk back.'

I pass Trev the joint. 'That does sound impressive,' I say.

'*Fuckin'* impressive,' Milton says. He and Trev nod like dogs in a car window. Now their heads have been set in motion I think they might not stop until they work loose and crash onto the tarmac.

'He must have been some guy, this Nibsey,' I say.

Smoke escapes from the corner of Trev's mouth like a trail of ectoplasm. He stops nodding and passes the joint to Milton. 'Nibsey wouldn't 'ave any messin' when he was doing his walk,' he says. 'Not even to pass him a can or a puff.'

'I saw him do the walk with a can in his hand,' Milton says.

'You couldn't 'ave,' Trev snaps. 'He wouldn't do that.'

'He did.'

'He didn't. He wouldn't be so stupid.'

They argue about this while I roll another joint.

When they run out of steam Trev flicks his lighter and

the flame singes the fur on his cuff. 'I remember once,' he says. 'Nibsey called a woman a stupid whore when she told him to get down. Wasn't any of her fuckin' business, she was going to the shop.'

'What was she going to buy?' Milton asks.

'I don't fuckin' know. Potatoes. Bread. What does it matter? She shouldn't have bothered Nibsey when he was doing his walk. He told her, though. He was the best rude person I've ever met in my life.'

I light the fresh joint, take a deep draw and hold it. Trev and Milton gawp. They must think I have lungs like bell jars. On the out breath I ask, 'Where is Nibsey? Is he still around? I'd like to see his walk.'

Trev picks up a handful of stones and throws one into the river – he stares at the ripples until they vanish and then throws another one.

'Nibsey don't walk no more,' Milton says.

A dog wanders down the bank, sniffs the grass and cocks his leg against a large rock that's on the edge of the shallow water.

Trev grabs another stone, lobs it at the dog and catches its side. It yelps and runs into the bushes. 'Fuckin' animal,' he mutters.'

'Piss off, 'Milton shouts. 'That's Nibsey's rock.'

'Creole'
Samantha Newbury

he said it was,
when the old man getting off the bus
asked what language he was speaking.
'It's a broken French.' And he resumed
his one-sided conversation.

My mind had already registered
the 'Frenchness' and had delved
amongst its archives
to dust off snatches learned
more than quarter of a century ago;
Creating dots of meaning
that somehow wouldn't *quite*
join into understanding.

Not French then, but Creole.
That explained the exotic twist
to the familiar, the dancing rhythm,
and, perhaps, the fact
that he said 'Yes' so much.

I have a star to prove it
Kate Noakes

I can be helpful in whatever way
you would find useful. I mean it, just say.

Yes, really. I have taken super-advanced
gymnastics and am quite well practised

at bending over barrels backwards
if it helps; or thrusting my hips outwards

to wrap and lock my legs behind my neck,
both of them, simultaneously back;

or ripping my shoulder from its joint
to squeeze into any box you point to.

Is there a particular one you
have in mind? A pigeon hole, might that do?

Or perspex for the show of it. Or is
there a round hole for me to square and kiss?

Do keep in mind, I am your flexible
friend, an employee so reliable,

I have a star to prove it.

The suicide note
Alicia Ogg

She called me at work.
She never calls me at work.
She called me to ask me
what I fancied for dinner.
I said I didn't mind.
She probably thought I didn't care
but I really didn't mind.
She said okay and she hung
up the phone.
I nearly called her back but
I thought it'd be fine.
I got back at the usual time
about half past six.
I went into the dining room
fixed myself a drink
and loosened my tie.
I thought she must be out.
It was then I noticed a folded
card resting against a Statue of Liberty
souvenir we'd bought on our honey moon.
It had my initial on the front.
I suddenly felt my heart take a jump.
A strange note.
It simply said,
I've taken three pork chops out
they're on top of the fridge.
I walked through to the kitchen
and there was a small pool of blood
where the chops had defrosted

and dripped onto the floor.
I heard a car pull into the driveway.
I thought it must be her.
I let out an odd sigh of relief and
I went to the front door.
When I saw that it was you
I knew I'd never see her again.
Now if you don't mind Officer
I'd like to go home.

Magic mirror
Valerie O'Riordan

A bowl of ammonia mixed with a cup of cornflour. Jemma beat them with the wooden spoon.

Mel watched. She said, 'That's it, look – the whatsit, the pneumonia, it's blending right in. I told yeh, yeh'll be Snow fuckin' White by dinner-time.' She watched Jemma dollop the runny paste onto her cheeks and smear it in, the rubber gloves dripping white liquid onto the ground. Like bird shit. 'Me brother won't know what hit him – look at yeh, the blushin' bride.'

'My face feels like it's burning,' said Jemma. Her eyes watered. 'How long do I leave it?'

Mel lit a fag and inhaled. The smell of wee was nauseating. 'Ah, well,' she said. 'Freckly skin like yours takes a real blast. If it's not dead sore, you're probably doin' it wrong.'

Jemma nodded. The skin on her left cheekbone began to blister.

Mel smiled. 'Aren't yeh just gorgeous?'

Why children's librarians shouldn't work alone
Emma Purshouse

Thursday. Mid morning, mid term.
There are no children here
just their stories and the silence.

The librarian re-reads *Snow White*
because once upon a time
this had been her favourite book,

this book where mirrors talk
and mothers order hearts of little girls
to be ripped out and eaten.

In the peripheries of vision,
shadows move amongst the shelves.
And draughts cause hairs to rise

on napes of necks. Nervous fingers
fidget through a well-cut bob
like bony combs. And panic

laces up the stays too tightly.
Fight or flight? She grabs the phone,
hisses out a cry for help,

I'm on my own! Dwarves, princes,
Christine from reference;
she doesn't care who comes to save her.

In the staff room, relieved, but still
on high alert, she eyes the apple
in her lunch box with suspicion.

It was the TV that got me
Leila Rasheed

The TV squats in the corner of the room, beholding us. It has been that way since Dad moved out, taking the remote control with him. Since then, it has failed to function. Friends say that new models can be had for half the price of a repair. They are missing the point.

Dad invited me over for lunch a few weeks after he moved out. It was important to be mature about these things, so he said. In the end I decided I should go, if only to get the remote control back. After all, I reasoned, I was an adult now. I had left home, so why shouldn't he?

She lives high up, in the flat Dad bought for her, with a swimming pool on the roof and a patent leather couch and green marble work-surfaces. You can see your face in every surface. I stood beside many versions of myself and circled a glass of cold champagne in my fingers. The liquid fizzed like a channel you can't get. Dad charged around, over-doing the host act, appearing and disappearing as he opened and closed mirror-plated doors to display en-suite, walk-in design features. She – the only one of us not reflected, except in my eyes – smiled and said she wanted to get to know me better. I mumbled something and wished she wasn't so attractive.

'What this place needs is a home entertainment system,' said Dad, during one of the more awkward silences.

'That reminds me,' I said. 'Dad...'

But he wasn't listening. He was measuring a wall, while she flicked through the John Lewis catalogue. At home, we only had an Argos catalogue, and even that was last year's. I put my glass down and left.

I came home to an empty house. Mum was at work, my brother and sister at school. I pushed the living room door open. No-one had opened the curtains that day and the room was dark. I stood there a long time, imagining myself the over-seer of a dark universe, full of indistinct solids and unutterable thoughts. Even though the TV was off I knew it was beholding me. I knew it beheld everything that came into its line of sight. I tried to out-stare it, but it had a grip that was unmasterable. When the television has nothing more to show you, it will show you yourself.

I phoned him some days later. I meant to ask about the remote control, but I did not get the chance. He overrode me as usual, switching to the sport without pausing to ask if I was watching the film (I was). He told me he needed my help to move the new television into her flat. It was important for everyone's sake to be very mature, so I said yes, of course. I circled a can of warm Coke in my hand as I spoke, sitting on the sofa and feeling the television's gaze upon me. The liquid buzzed like a fly behind glass; trapped. I watched the dark person inside the television who was me, and realised with a sinking feeling that I would do whatever it wanted, whatever that was.

The new television was sleek and flat and wide and had a plastic skin congealed across its black space. I had to stagger with it clasped in my arms like an oddly-shaped dance partner. We negotiated the lobby, the lift, the landing. I carried it into the living room, she backing away from me with grateful coos and directions and *mind my mirrors*. It was then that I realised I was mistaken. Our television certainly had a purpose in mind, but it was not concerned with me, any more than the universe is concerned with a single comet.

It was a pleasant revelation, like finally understanding an elusive mathematical concept. Smiling, I carried the new television past the area designed for it, full across the room and through the open window I lifted it. I heard them shouting behind me, but I did not turn. I let my aching arms relax and I let go. It fell thirteen stories, it fell like a waterfall of 24 hour news, like confetti of advertisements, like a bomb full of East Enders, the air signalling around it until it burst in a perfect explosion of nothing.

A few days later I found the remote control, down the back of the sofa.

Mnemonic
Jacqui Rowe

She remembers there were six
remembers eating Arnold Bennett at the Ritz,
unadulterated, over-egged, and buttery
with haddock, smokes out the when
they knew what money was
a Sole Colbert and Crepes Suzette memento
how full-mouthed he guinea vowelled
her silent ha'penny *e*, plain Anne to Anna, queen
and empress of all five towns, he said, until she saved
his stumble, served him her mnemonic present. Now
in darkness, chasing sleepy dwarfs, the final
samurai, wonders beyond the hanging
gardens and the mausoleum, she remembers
choosing brandy flambéed Lobster Thermidor
said his name as sweet heart just that once
calls back Stoke and Hanley first
then Burslem, Fenton, Longton, Tunstall
all the six.

At the bus stop
Rosie Sandler

When she said they were
'all right at that age'
(pointing to a small girl (black)
I said, 'black or white, they're all right
at any age – if they're all right.'
And she looked at me slantwise
like I was a puzzle
she'd like to put straight.
Jewish
I could have whispered
if she'd known what to ask.

Lucky boys
Sandra Tappenden

Swagger :
They wag their shadows along the hollow pavement
all mooch and taunt like the sports instructor never existed
or maybe because his constant ear-bashing sets off
a kind of ringing in the marrow – Go! Go!
a shot of mercury in the muscle – we are men!
They aren't but no-one can be entirely certain

Play:
Can we have a cat in the play? That's his secret weapon
his pussy weapon (I think they mean Suki next door
the tortoiseshell charmer) Steve 'n' Joe
have been a bit – what ? Distant? Stupid? Mean?
Picky or harsh or rubbish as co-directors?
I like the cat actor idea but fear the consequences

Girls:
Go on then – they lean back against a shaded car
the boys not quite up to whatever it is
it's a dare they've dreamed about dimly
a preface to grappling and mockery or worse
one has hair like a girl and is more beautiful
the others know it as they will damage and shame

The illiterate man
Val Thompson

I have been in the dark,
been in the dark,
all this time
I have held onto a secret,
held onto a secret,
all this time.
I have avoided so many actions,
avoided actions,
all this time.
Wriggled round so many occasions,
occasion after occasion,
all this time.
I have felt the fear of discovery,
felt fear,
all this time.
Enacted and re-enacted exposure,
practised exposure,
all this time.
I have seen words but not known them,
not known words,
all this time.
I have dreamed of the light,
dreamed of reading in the light,
all this time,
all this time.

Overdraft limit
Susie Wild

I am not going to spend
    £4
on a giant
      pencil.
I am made of money
but I draw the line
    at *that*.
With a small pencil.
That didn't cost £4.

'You aren't going to fucking do that, are you?'
Philip Williams

When I pass on an errand, an hour after,
I'm struck that she has done so, climbed onto
a black sill, prised open a leaded, latticed
window, not quite wide enough to squeeze through.

There are neighbours with ladders, shouting
advice and the man opposite calling back
to his companion along the garden path
to fetch the long-handled screwdriver.

As the high school closes, I find that this
not quite perfect, not quite picture-postcard
cottage with its for-sale sign, its drive now
empty of BMW and Audi,

has latch-key daughters. Their lock-out reveals
the youngest's coarseness, the sixth-form eldest's
enterprise. I drop my eyes as she squats
and the high sill widens for her to dangle

her white thighs, sway and kick
her bare feet as at a poolside.

Snap
Jude d'Souza

'...And if you need any more proof it's not a romantic thing, her grandmother might be joining us.' I tell Rob indignantly before hanging up the phone and returning to my greasy café breakfast. Across from me I spy a girl about my age scribbling away at a pad while her panini goes cold, her mobile vibrating frantically beside it.

As soon as she answers I'm back on the prowl, ears pricked for any fascinating morsels of conversation that might drift my way and inspire me.

'No, the train isn't for another ten minutes. How's Isis doing?'

Boring

'Yeah, she's been a bit temperamental since the vet...'

Boring

'A bird? Ugh. I hope you've disinfected. But that's a good sign, it means she's warming to you.'

Not great, but maybe...

'Trust me, a dead body in the hall usually means she's trying to impress you.'

OK, now that could work really well out of context...

Before the precise phrasing escapes me, I grab my pen and jot it down on the nearest paper-like object, which happens to be a serviette.

I glance up again to find her staring purposefully across at me. I do my best to affect an air of nonchalance and pretend I'm deeply engrossed in finishing some sort of napkin-based essay. It's probably fair to say my best isn't very good. I fight the urge to gulp when a shadow falls ominously over my table.

'Were you just eavesdropping on my conversation?'

My heart goes cold.

'Sort of. Well, more like...uh...No, not in, like, a bad sort of...' a panicked tangle of words tumble out. 'Um, is it too late for me to be indignant about that accusation?'

'May I ask *why* you were eavesdropping?'

'It's a...Like a...um...A sort of writing project thingy that...uh...'

'Bugged?'

'Bugged, yes. Wait, how do you...?'

'Me too.'

'Oh.'

Author information and websites

This book doesn't include author biographies because we wanted each writer to have an equal shot at your attention; also for reasons of time and space (as Einstein might say). However, most of our writers have a website or blog where you can learn more about them, read their work and find out where to hear them read in the flesh.

Please visit our own site **www.bugged.org.uk**, or find us on Facebook (Bugged) and Twitter (BuggedProject) to let us know which writers you enjoyed most. You never know who's listening ...

Jenn Ashworth	jennashworth.co.uk
Mollie Baxter	molliebaxter.com
Jo Bell	jobell.org.uk *or*
	belljarblog.wordpress.com
Julie Boden	julieboden.co.uk
Cathy Bryant	cathybryant.co.uk
David Calcutt	davidcalcutt.co.uk
Helen Calcutt	poetryataria.wordpress.com
Steph Dale	stephdale.com
Lucy Douglas	west-linton.org.uk/content/
	pentlands-writers-lucy-douglas
Jo Field	wordaid.blogspot.com
Marilyn Francis	circaidygregory.co.uk/poetry.htm
David Gaffney	davidgaffney.weebly.com
Sarah Gallagher	sarahgracegallagher.blogspot.com
Ruskin Gammon	hullblog.wordpress.com
Roz Goddard	rozgoddard.com
Andy Jackson	soutarwriters.co.uk/andyjackson
	or northcarrlight.blogspot.com
Sarah James	sarah-james.co.uk
Charlie Jordan	charliejordan.co.uk
Calum Kerr	calumkerr.co.uk *or*
	unmitigated-audacity.blogspot.com

Emma Lannie	garglingwithvimto.blogspot.com
Rob A Mackenzie	robmack.blogspot.com
Stuart Maconie	stuartmaconie.com
Ian Marchant	ianmarchant.wordpress.com
Lynsey May	lynseymay.com
Mil Millington	mil-millington.com
Emma Morgan	booglarise.blogspot.com
Benjamin Morris	forpub.com
Kate Noakes	boomslangpoetry.co.uk
Valerie O'Riordan	not-exactly-true.blogspot.com
Emma Purshouse	emmapurshouse.co.uk
Leila Rasheed	leilarasheed.com
Jacqui Rowe	jacquirowe.com
Sandra Tappenden	thelampandtheworm.blogspot.com
Susie Wild	brightyoungthings.info *or* myspace.com/soozerama